Early Praise for

BRAIN
STORM

"*BrainStorm* is a masterful autobiography about Sara Schley's lived experiences with bipolar disorder II, poignantly capturing the danger of years of misdiagnosis, the perils of antidepressant monotherapy, and the lack of understanding about bipolar spectrum disorders in the psychiatric community. This is an essential and hugely helpful first-person narrative account of what it is like to live with BD II that will increase awareness and decrease stigma and inspire others who struggle with BD II. I fervently hope that the book is read by a wide audience."

—DR. HOLLY SWARTZ, Professor of Psychiatry, University of Pittsburgh

"I vividly remember reading *BrainStorm* for the first time, reaching page three, and breaking into tears. Here was someone describing exactly how I felt, as if they were inside of my brain, at a time when I didn't even understand what I was feeling. It wouldn't be an overstatement to say this book changed, if not saved, my life, for which I am forever grateful."

—JAMES HARRISON, University of California Berkeley Sophomore

"I read *BrainStorm* straight through while standing in the kitchen. This is a very compelling, very important memoir about the 'other' bipolar disorder—the one hardly anyone knows about."

—DR. JAMES PHELPS, Psychiatrist, Author of *A Spectrum Approach to Mood Disorders*

"I haven't been able to stop reading *BrainStorm*. The writing is riveting, captivating, and breathtakingly painful and courageous. Wow. Thank you!"

—JAI KELLER, Licensed Mental Health Counselor

"Captivated, I read *BrainStorm* in two sittings last weekend. I couldn't put it down. While I have not experienced bipolar first-hand, I am a caregiver of someone who is paranoid schizophrenic. Sara Schley's book showed me a whole new way of thinking about her and what she is living through. While not bipolar II, she is fighting her own demons. You've opened a whole new place for her in my heart and for that I am profoundly thankful."

—LEANNE GRILLO, Business Consultant

"*BrainStorm* is a riveting, insightful, gut-wrenching, and ultimately hope-filled book. I literally could not put it down. Sara Schley has so much to teach us in her life story. She is an inspiration!"

—DARCY WINSLOW, Former head of Nike Women's Worldwide

"Sara Schley courageously uses the power of her raw experience with depression to point a way toward hope. After years of misdiagnoses by medical professionals, she finds a psychiatrist who recognizes bipolar II. *BrainStorm* is a testament to living well with bipolar II and is a wake-up call for doctors and all who struggle with depression that may be misdiagnosed."

—MARA BRIGHT, Teacher and Librarian

"*BrainStorm* is a vividly told personal journey of emotional devastation, dogged perseverance, healing, and growth. Sara Schley unabashedly relied on a web of support and guidance from family, friends, and professionals. Her journey is a testament to the power of vulnerability and reaching for connection."

—PAUL DOUD, Marriage and Family Therapist

"I wish I had read *BrainStorm* before, before my dear nephew gave in to bipolar II despair. If I had read it, if my family had read it then, he would be alive now, sharing his loving genius with the world. This well-researched personal story is a life-changer for anyone stricken with bipolar II disorder and those who love them enough to help."

—KITTY AXELSON-BERRY, Publisher and Personal
    Historian

"Sara Schley has written an absorbing and disturbing memoir that shines a harsh light on the incredible challenges of getting appropriate treatment for mental health challenges, given our fragmented mental health-care system, as well as the appalling ignorance of some professionals. All mental health professionals should read this book, as it proves how important it is that we stay informed about current knowledge in our field so that we can 'do no harm' to our clients. But perhaps, more important, it presents a poignant illustration of the vital importance of listening to and taking good care of our clients who come to us in their time of most desperate need."

—NANCY ROOSA, PsyD, Pediatric Neuropsychologist

BRAIN
STORM

SARA
SCHLEY

BRAIN
STORM

*From Broken to Blessed
on the Bipolar Spectrum*

BrainStorm: From Broken to Blessed on the Bipolar Spectrum

For information about this title or to order other books and/or electronic media, contact the publisher:

Bear Mountain Press
www.saraschley.com
info@saraschley.com

ISBNs:
979-8-9851828-2-8 (hardcover)
979-8-9851828-0-4 (softcover)
979-8-9851828-1-1 (eBook)

Printed in the United States of America

Cover and Interior design: 1106 Design

For my grandfather Lewis Wald and my mother,
Harriet Wald Schley, who wrestled with their own
BrainStorms. Your lives were a blessing;
the healing here is in your name.

And for millions unknown, caught in the terror of
a BrainStorm: May you find peace and healing.

DISCLAIMER

I am choosing to tell my bipolar spectrum story now to help end the stigma, reduce suffering, and save lives. Here are two important disclaimers:

First, my story is that of a middle-class white woman with significant privilege. Not everyone who reads this book will have access to the resources that my race and economic status have afforded me. If you are a member of a traditionally marginalized community and on the bipolar spectrum, I hope that my story will help you feel less alone because—despite our differences—you and I share a similar brain pattern. I hope the resources here will serve you.

Second, I am not a psychologist, psychiatrist, or any other mental health professional. The opinions here are based on my own experiences and should not in any way be considered as medical advice. Please use this book in conjunction with a professional you trust.

If you are experiencing a mental health emergency, please call 911 or go to your nearest Emergency Room.

CONTENTS

PROLOGUE

"The disease feeds on shame, shame feeds on silence,
and I will not be silent anymore."
—TERRI CHENEY

We're hurtling down I-95 South, heading to Naples, Florida, to visit my brother Bill and sister-in-law Annie for winter break. It's the third day of the drive and the four of us—Joe, me, and our twins, Sam and Maya, have settled into a rhythm, switching drivers every couple of hours. The kids are now hanging out with earbuds and laptops, Maya in the backseat, Sam next to me. The driver gets to pick the podcast.

Sam and Maya are almost seventeen. They've had their licenses for just shy of six months, with most of their driving careers spent on backcountry roads. The white-knuckle shift each of them just had—driving seventy in pouring rain on a two-lane highway in South Carolina surrounded by eighteen-wheelers—was an initiation into a new level of driving prowess. They're feeling primed for action. Our Honda Pilot tank is full, and I'm tanked up on two Dunkin' mocha lattes. This is a twenty-four-hour trek. Caffeine powered, I'm determined to deliver us to our destination for the night, Gainesville, Florida, five hours away.

I'm happy to have the teens captive in the car for a few days. Their lives are so full these days, with commitments to an academically driven high school, sports, friends, clubs, plus their new licenses. Not to mention Instagram, Snapchat, and whatever other new social media craze of the hour has emerged, filling their every waking moment. The spaciousness of this time together without an agenda feels luxurious. And though I'm hoping for some meaningful conversation, I know better than to force it.

Just outside of Georgia, the subject comes up. Maybe it was because the rhythm of the windshield wipers had us mesmerized. Or because the kids were wired, yet spent from their share of the drive. Or because they'd simply run out of chats to snap for the moment. Sam was sitting next to me, riding shotgun instead of in the back seat on buds. Maybe that helped.

"Guys, do you remember I told you I wrote a memoir on my experience with bipolar, called *BrainStorm*?"

"Yes," they answered in unison and without that absentminded hesitation I've learned means they're pretending to listen. A rare present moment of full attention, times two.

"There's something I'd like your opinion on, and it begins with a bit of a story."

"OK, Mom, phone down," Sam says with a grin.

"You know how I go on my women's whitewater Deerfield River paddle every summer in August?"

"Yup."

"There's a friend of mine who always comes. The paddle is exhilarating, always leaving us a bit high in the best way, and we celebrate with my once-a-year beer and burger at The People's Pint afterward. We were checking in over home brew and I asked my friend, who seems constitutionally upbeat, how her summer was.

"She said it hadn't be great. Then she told me something that made my heart stop. Her sister's son had taken his own life in May after being very depressed. He had been diagnosed with bipolar years ago.

"I'm not sure why, because usually I hesitate to be 'out' about my brain, but without missing a beat I told her, 'I'm also bipolar, bipolar II.'

"She was surprised. Most people who know me as energetic and positive are. She asked when it first happened, how long I'd known my diagnosis, and so on."

I couldn't see the kids' reactions because it was dark and rainy, but I sensed they were paying attention.

"I told my friend how sorry I was," I continued. "'It's such a cruel disease.' Then I told her about my memoir, and that I'd given it to some friends to read. She said something that kind of blew me away. 'Sara, did you know that my business for decades was a private publishing service specializing in memoirs? I'd love to see your manuscript.'

"I said I hadn't read it in a long time. That I wrote much of it ten years ago. I even said, 'I think it kind of sucks.'

"She said, 'Let me be the judge of that. Send it and I'll take a look.'

"I sent her the short version—and she called me the next day. She said if she had read my manuscript six months ago, her nephew might still be alive. That my memoir would save lives, and she would edit it for free in honor of her nephew.

"'Wow,' I thought. 'What an offer.'

"I had told myself I couldn't publish the book until my parents—Gramma and Grandpa—were gone, because there's a lot of Gramma's story here. Now they are. I also told myself I wouldn't publish it until you guys were old enough to understand and give me your consent. Now you are."

I stopped talking for a moment, my breath stuck on an inhale. Maya and Sam were uncharacteristically silent, listening to every word.

"I want to know what you think," I continued with an exhale. "I'm in a dilemma about whether to do this. On the one hand, you have my friend's super generous offer. You have the fact that the way has been cleared with Gramma and Grandpa passed on. You have the knowledge that the manuscript really could help people. Maybe a lot of people. Save lives. And you have the opportunity in me as an author to destigmatize the disease. Yes, bipolar can look like this: a woman who is blessed with a full and rich life as a professional, mother, wife, and more.

"On the other hand, you have that stigma. I don't want you to be embarrassed by me. I may be putting my career in jeopardy. So many people still have deep prejudice against mental illness, and they blame the victim. They fear and mistrust people with the bipolar label. Coming out of the closet with the truth of my history could put me on the receiving end of that kind of '—ism.' It could tarnish my professional reputation, cost me clients, some livelihood, your college tuition! I keep going back and forth on what I should do. To publish or not to publish? What do you guys think?"

Zero hesitation.

"You have to do it, Mom," Maya said.

"Absolutely, no question," Sam echoed simultaneously.

"Mom, you really could save lives! What else is more important?!"

"Who cares what other people think of you! Tell the truth."

"You know, it's kind of like sexual orientation," Sam continued, "Your generation cares about it; we don't."

"Yeah, attitudes are changing about mental health," Maya said. "A lot of kids we know are on meds. A lot of kids have anxiety. Kids cut themselves. Kids admit they're suicidal. We learn about this stuff in health class and we all just kind of accept it. Don't worry, Mom, people won't judge you! Mom, you have to do this!"

My heart swelled with gratitude: for the goodness of these kids and for this moment in time when I could be fully open with them. I felt relieved at no longer having to hide the whole truth of my story from them. They knew part of my story, but they didn't know my *full* story. I had been protecting them. I had never wanted them to know what I had gone through, or to be afraid for their own brains. I felt so much pride in that moment, driving through Georgia with the car's headlights piercing the dark. Pride at their generosity of spirit and their commitment to doing the right thing to help others. It was almost enough, that moment right there, their championing of me and this cause.

But then I realized that to fulfill their aspirations for me, to merit this level of enthusiasm and respect from them, I would have to say "yes." Yes, to laying my soul bare and telling the raw truth and sharing a story full of sorrow and redemption. And so I am. And so I have.

INTRODUCTION

For twenty-five years, I wrestled with a demon. A merciless perpetrator of terror who would emerge from the shadows and abduct me to his realm. I could not anticipate his timing or comprehend his motives or why he chose me as victim. I could never understand what I'd done to provoke his wrath. Like Persephone in the Underworld, I was caught in the grip of a force I could not overcome. For months on end, I was a prisoner of darkness. I don't literally believe in demons or hell, but this is what it felt like on the inside.

The brutality I was experiencing is commonly referred to as depression. But that word does not begin to explain the cruelty of the disease that would bring me to my knees, begging for mercy. I went to the precipice of death, believing that only there would I finally find relief for my broken brain.

I finally learned that the brain pattern I carry is a genetic anomaly on the bipolar spectrum known as bipolar II. The Roman numeral "II" is the critical distinction in understanding, diagnosing, and treating it. And *it can* be treated effectively. There is hope. There is relief. My demons have finally been confined to the underworld, where they belong. Their captive has been freed.

The tragedy is that millions of people with bipolar II go untreated, and their lives are destroyed. For many reasons that I describe in this book, bipolar II and other bipolar spectrum disorders are usually missed in diagnosis. People suffering from bipolar II are among the homeless, the addicts, the alcoholics, those tormented in psych wards, and the electric-shocked. Their families are ruined, their loved ones brokenhearted.

I would have been there, too, had it not been for a combination of luck, love, dedicated healers, and effective medicines to treat the chemical imbalance in my brain.

My life was saved. I offer you this book with the prayer that it may give you the hope, knowledge, and power to save your own precious life or the life of someone you love dearly.

—*Sara Schley*
October 2021

PART ONE

BrainStorm:

FROM BROKEN TO BLESSED ON THE BIPOLAR SPECTRUM

CHAPTER I

THE BRAIN: AS VAST AS THE COSMOS AND EQUALLY UNCHARTED

I wake up at 5:00 a.m., sandwiched between my daughter and my husband. It's the year 2007 and I'm forty-six years old. There is a new moon in the predawn winter sky. I slip out of bed without waking them and draw my morning tub, filling it with lavender, rose, and eucalyptus oils. Thirty minutes of jet therapy later, I ascend to my "tower," an eight-foot-square room, up a staircase from our bedroom, that I've dedicated to yoga, prayer, and meditation. I stretch each morning to Hebrew chants, moving my body slowly and rhythmically to the music, feeling each muscle ease into the morning. Two hours later I'll wake the twins, Maya and Sam, with gentle kisses. "Get up for school guys, time to get dressed and eat breakfast, gotta catch the bus. Dress warm, it's winter-cold out there." They're now four years past infancy, and I still love the smell of their heads, the scent of innocence and dreams. I inhale as I hug them, my vitamins M and S.

I pick out clothes for work. This afternoon I'll be flying to Chicago for a meeting, and I want to look sharp. It's a conservative setting, so I'll dress respectably but with flair: gray skirt and matching jacket from EILEEN FISHER, dark purple silk sweater, Klimt scarf, boots, jade earrings, and a necklace from the Red Sea.

I turn my focus to the kids. Breakfast, boots, coats, hats, gloves, and hugs later, and they are off to kindergarten. I kiss Joe goodbye before he drives to his new job with an entrepreneurial dot.com in New Hampshire. Since my flight is much later, I head up the hill with my beloved old yellow lab, Starhawk, to meet a friend for a walk. Leah and I have crampons on our shoes and carry ski poles. It's icy. We walk down to the brook and then alongside it through the woods, three miles. It's exceptionally beautiful in February, as every day's changing temperature, humidity, and wind combine to create new ice sculptures. Water flows under ice and around a hard rock ledge, giving a womb-like soundtrack to this walk.

After our walk I'll put on my work clothes, pack my computer, palm, cell phone, and Bluetooth, and head to the airport. But I'll stop by Swift River School to hug Sam and Maya. They'll wrap themselves around me and smother me with kisses––still too young to hide their affection from peers. "We love you, Mom! We can't stop hugging you."

An unremarkable scene from a midlife working mom who lives in rural Massachusetts and is blessed with a flexible schedule, a supportive husband, healthy twins, and a strong sense of gratitude for all that life gives her. It sounds like an enviable, maybe even outrageously luxurious life.

Unless you know what was happening in this same life less than six months prior.

It sounds melodramatic, but here's the truth: Death was at my door hour by hour. I was in the throes of an uncontrollable depression, unable to get out of bed, dreaming about suicide as a welcome relief. Each hour of my life, if you can even call it that, was a painful reminder that another hour of excruciating existence would come, and then another, and then another. I had been suffering for a long time with an undiagnosed disease of the brain. It had sapped my intellect, energy, and spirit. I didn't know what was going on.

My brain had stopped working. I couldn't add simple numbers, do the dishes, dress my kids, or make them lunch. I was unable to respond to emails, return phone calls, or write a coherent sentence. My characteristic humor was gone. Smiling was painful for the muscles in my face. My libido was gone. I stopped washing my hair because it took too much energy to remember how to do it. My fingers were bloody because I was addicted to ripping my cuticles.

The cruel voice inside my head chanted at me relentlessly: "Your family would be better off if you were dead." I could think only of impending catastrophes: We'd get in a car accident driving down our icy hill; Joe would lose his job; I'd never make love, play sports, or enjoy friends again. The world was being poisoned by toxic chemicals, and global warming was going to kill us all anyway.

My kids, who were four years old at that time, had no idea what was going on with Mom, except that she was no fun anymore. She wouldn't play any games with them, didn't even have the energy to take them outside, and mostly wanted to sleep. My choices seemed to be a psych ward, electroconvulsive therapy, or suicide. My husband and family were trying to decide if they should check me into a locked psych ward at the hospital in Holyoke or try shock therapy. Somewhere in the recesses of my mind, I knew I couldn't leave my four-year-olds with the legacy of a mother who had died by suicide. Although I was barely alive and wanted to stop the pain forever, I couldn't choose death over my children.

How had I come to this state with a loving husband, the twins of my dreams, circles of friends, and fulfilling work—a life of enviable abundance, and privilege? I wasn't suffering from everyday depression. It wasn't situational. I wasn't sad. I hadn't experienced a painful loss of a loved one. I didn't have posttraumatic stress disorder from a near-death accident. I wasn't a victim of incest, rape, or abuse.

I have an anomaly in my DNA, an accident of genetics I now know is bipolar II or "soft bipolar." Ninety percent of the time, this disease is misdiagnosed as "standard depression." It presents with the classic symptoms: exhaustion, negativity, hopelessness, loss of joy in life. But this diagnosis is the kiss of death for a bipolar brain like mine—and for those of millions of people in this country alone who suffer from bipolar II. Here's why: The standard meds for depression—SSRIs (selective serotonin reuptake inhibitors) like Prozac, Lexapro, Paxil, and Zoloft—are poison to the bipolar brain. They actually make us sicker: more anxious, more psychotic, and more willing to act on suicidal thoughts. This was true for me. The depressions I'd suffered from on and off for twenty-five years without medication had become dangerously worse when I was on Lexapro and Prozac.

What makes bipolar II hard to diagnose is that people with it don't show the classic signs of mania associated with bipolar I, also known as manic-depressive disorder. Even though they are wired similarly and respond similarly to standard medications, they don't have its insatiable highs. Classic signs of mania include needing only a few hours of sleep a night, going on spending sprees, having insatiable sexuality, and incessant speech.

This pattern is so common that we use it colloquially to describe people. When you hear someone say, "That guy's really manic," you know it means he's some combination of hyperactive and nonstop talking. If a fast-talking, fidgeting person with "manic" behavior bounces from high speed in one phase to darkly depressed in another, we're not surprised if they return from a psychiatrist with a diagnosis of bipolar and a script for lithium to treat it.

Although I've never had any of these classically manic symptoms, I've always had more energy than most people. In high school I was awarded the Harvard Book Prize for the top schol-ar-athlete in my graduating class of five hundred. Harvard had been awarding these prizes in high schools around the country for years, but mine was the first they'd ever given to a female student. I got 800s on the SATs in math and earned As in calculus. I went to Brown University. As an undergrad, I biked to classes, studied four hours straight every night, and then headed to the pool for a one-mile swim followed by midnight drinks with my friends. I maintained a 4.0 in science, acing physics and organic chemistry, and I started as a right wing in varsity field hockey in my freshman year. I had a blast in college, thriving on the athletic competition, the intellectual challenge, my feisty women friends, and a sense that nothing but success and accolades lay ahead.

Then, out of nowhere, a door slammed on my life. On the morning of my twenty-first birthday, I couldn't get out of bed. I was suddenly immobilized. I was a senior in college. There was no precedent for this and there had been no warning. My legs were too heavy to raise from under the blankets. I did not want to see friends, did not want to get dressed, could barely get up to lug myself to class. (Not one to skip class, I did drag myself there.) That afternoon, my brothers and sister, all older than me, drove from Boston to surprise me on my birthday. The three of them hid under the covers of my double bed and gleefully yelled, "Surprise!" when I got back from class.

Instead of delight, I felt terror and shame. I did not recognize myself in this state of flat affect combined with a sense of doom, and I didn't want Martha, Bill, and Dan to see me like this.

They took me out for a celebratory dinner that night, pasta and beer at a favorite Italian restaurant in East Providence. My family is a boisterous crew; it's impossible to finish a sentence without being interrupted. We're too enthusiastic about our ideas to wait for a break in the action. I barely spoke a word that night, despite generous toasts and proclamations for my bright future now that graduation was on the horizon. I'd already been accepted by an Ivy League medical school. The conversation switched from me to the Bruins (love 'em), Ronald Reagan (hate 'im), and our parents' upcoming thirty-fifth wedding anniversary.

Given the hardy competition for airtime, my sibs didn't notice my silence. They departed for the one-hour drive north to Boston close to midnight. I felt both relieved and empty. Relieved that I would not have to make the physically exhausting effort of trying to appear normal. And empty, more alone than I'd ever been in my life. I sat down and sketched a stick figure of a girl at the bottom of a valley surrounded by ominous mountains, reaching up, beseeching, with no one to respond to her cries for help. That was me.

For the next month, I wrestled. It was as if some force had beaten me, pulled a plug at my core and drained my zest for life, leaving me zombie-like. My expressive face became flat, my emotions monochromatic, my ability to conjure positive futures gone. I was graduating a semester ahead of my classmates and dragged myself to the only class I needed to pass to finish college.

During most of my time at Brown, I'd always sat in the first couple of rows of the lecture halls so I could focus. Now I sat as far from the professor as possible, in the cold wooden chairs of the balcony of a cavernous lecture hall, slumped over, too exhausted to sit up straight while my religious studies professor, an ancient, crotchety Ivy League stereotype with a tweed coat and an upper-class Yankee accent, droned on about something I could barely understand.

In the end, I scraped by with a C minus. After sixteen years of school, it was the first time I'd ever received anything less than a B. The truth is, that passing grade was a gift I didn't deserve because I really didn't know anything about the material. In the month since my birthday, I had learned nothing. I could not focus, could not concentrate, could not recall words or concepts or facts. My typical self-discipline and ease with academics had vanished, replaced by an unfocused mind that I had no experience with and didn't understand.

What had happened to my good brain? Who was this "alien" who had seized my life? I suddenly had more compassion for people with learning disabilities and chronic low grades. But I sure didn't want to be one of them. I wanted this nightmare of me with the dysfunctional brain to be over. Terrified, I wanted to wake up to the feisty, smart, easy self I identified with as "me."

Yet, hour after hour, the nightmare continued. I slogged through life torn in two from the inside. I had no love for anything, yet I missed my *joie de vivre*. I lost all interest in friends, yet I craved time with them. I stopped biking to class but hungered for the exhilaration of physical activity. All I wanted to do was sleep, but rest alluded me because I felt guilty and ashamed for spending my days sleeping. I lived inside an excruciating paradox: Whatever I chose to do in any moment, I was sure I should be doing the opposite. If I were home in Boston with family, I wanted to be in Providence with friends. If I were out with friends, I wanted to be home by myself. And if I were home by myself, I felt painfully lonely. No choice was ever right.

My siblings sent word to our mother after visiting me on my birthday. My mother, then fifty-seven, looked fifteen years younger. Like her own mother, she had gone to Wellesley College (class of 1947). She carried the demeanor of a well-bred Yankee: elegantly dressed, well-spoken, quick-witted, and politically astute. She wrote crisp letters to the editor whenever she found their prose or positions to be below her standards.

With all her good looks, charm, and intelligence, my mother didn't have much use for feelings. In her world, stoicism was of greater value than feelings. You didn't "air your dirty laundry" and didn't talk about emotions.

I am six years old, living in a dark, musty Cape Cod cottage. There are weathered gray shingles and a handful of dusty muntin windows that don't let in the sun. There is green mold growing on the windowsills. My brown hair is in pigtails that haven't been combed in days. I'm wearing a red T-shirt and a pair of my brother Dan's cut-off blue jeans that I keep up with a thin nylon rope tied around my waist.

"Mom, I'm hungry."

"You'll have to get yourself something to eat." My mother's voice is tired, almost lifeless.

I use both hands, lean back, and open the fridge, but I don't see much. There is a bottle of Coke. One cool thing about this house is that it has a bottle opener right on the cabinet, and I can reach it. I open the Coke and take a swig. It is sweet and cold.

"Can we go to South Beach today?"

No answer.

I go to the door of her room to see what's going on. My mother is glued to the bed. My father is working in Boston all week. I have no idea where my brothers and sister are. Just gone. I'm alone with this empty shell of a mother. The lively, pretty, brown-eyed mom who liked to take me shopping for clothes and read me books has disappeared. I don't know why or when she'll be back.

Every day, reaching for sunlight, I escape on my blue banana boat bike and head for the beach alone. My mom never asks me where I'm going.

My family is building a house on the beach about a mile away. I'm pretty fast on my bike, so it takes me only ten minutes to get there. I can smell the salt air as I get closer. I like to sit on a rock near the gray foundation and watch the men work. They have big muscles and are dark tan, probably from working outside all day. They are pouring concrete to make a cellar. There is a fresh, warm breeze blowing off the ocean. I feel safe here in the light of the sun and sound of the waves. I guess I don't bother the workmen, and they let me hang out there. I stay for most of the day.

As it begins to get colder, I realize I should head home. I'm a little hungry too. The ride home is easier because it's downhill, so I get there fast. My heart hopes that my mom will be up to greet me with her warm smile and a glass of milk. But my mom is still in bed. She never asks where I've been. I guess I'll have to find something to eat. There is bread in the green tin bread box and some peanut butter on the shelf. I find a knife and spread it. It's a little hard to spread the peanut butter. It makes some holes in the bread. It's OK, it still tastes good.

There's not much to do. Luckily, I have a record of Mary Poppins, the first movie I'd ever seen in a movie theatre. We'd watched it last summer when it came out. I love that record, and I know how to lift the needle up on the little record player and start it. "Supercalifragilistic-expialadocious, even though the sound of it is something quite atrocious, if you say it loud enough you'll always sound . . ." I don't remember how to say the next word. My mom looks like Mary Poppins when she's happy. I like to look at the record cover.

Later that evening I'm lying in my single bed under the covers. My mom comes to my bedside and sits on the edge. "Sara, I know this might be hard for you to hear, but I'm leaving your father."

I'm sad and scared by the news. At first. But I didn't know then that she'd tell me this story many times over the next weeks and months. She never leaves. I stop believing her.

It is 1974 and I'm a thirteen-year-old high school freshman. I've watched my mom wrestling with depression all through my grow-ing-up years.

When I graduated from elementary school, she decided to go back to school to get her master's degree in social work. I guess the work-load was too demanding, but I didn't really pay too much attention because I was busy with my friends, sports, and school. She finds it hard to concentrate on the homework, can't focus or finish chapters. I don't understand this—it's easy for me to get my homework done. She stops going to class.

I know she's in trouble one afternoon when I come home from school early because field hockey is rained out. She's in bed. The room is pitch black and the curtains are drawn. I see the pills by her bed encased in a cardboard wrapper. I never understand why they put that scary picture on the cover, the one that looks like a mad woman literally pulling her hair out. How can that make a depressed person feel better? I suspect it is a way for the drug company to make her feel bad, so she'll need more of that drug.

We don't cry or show fear in my household, but we're somehow allowed to get mad. I'm mad that my mom is absent from my life. I'm mad that she seems to have no control over this thing. I'm mad that she loses energy and focus and turns cold. I don't raise my voice or rage like my dad, but I'm snide and disrespectful, and I know, mean. I can't seem to help myself. I have to blame someone. The muscles in my neck get tight and I spew it out.

"Why don't you just get up and deal with your life, Mom? Jesus, you've been telling me you're leaving Dad for a decade, yet you just sit here and take his abuse. No wonder you're depressed. Finish school, get a job, do something!"

She doesn't answer. Just turns away.

She is weak and lazy, and I can't stand to be around her. I feel her mood sucking the air out of the room, and it's almost as if I have to get outside to breathe. I dial my best friend, Martha.

"Can you meet me at Eliot Park?"

"Sure."

With that, I am gone.

My mother had suffered from depression on and off since I was a baby. I remember each occurrence vividly, starting from the time I was six on Cape Cod. She had been on lithium since I was a young teen. When I was twenty-one, still seeking my place in the world separate from my parents, she was the woman in the family with mental illness. I defined myself as her opposite: I was the competitive athlete, the liberated woman, the mountain-scaling adventurer. Above all, I was upbeat, and never constitutionally negative, as I'd seen her at her worst.

Her father had also been a victim of debilitating depressions. This was in the 1940s and 1950s, when no one talked about such things. My mother's mother had always been upbeat, cheerful, positive, and bright, never hinting at what it might have been like to live with a man who was president of his company and a pillar in the community, but so sick with depression that he underwent electric shock treatment. My grandmother maintained her dignity and grace throughout all that.

From her parents, my mother learned the Yankee way: show no emotion. I referred to her as a "Yankee Jew," the oxymoron intentional. She was Jewish by identity and heritage, but Yankee by training and practice. Her mother's side of the family had been in Boston since the late 1800s, long before most European Jews immigrated to the US; her mother had graduated from Wellesley College in 1919. Her father had gone to Harvard. At their home, people did not raise their voices, nor express emotion. Sharp intellect, witty remarks, and steady composure were valued.

After graduation, she'd met my father, also Jewish, in New York City, and they'd married the following year. She became an archetypical post-World War II suburban housewife, mother of four baby boomer kids, with a Navy vet husband who worked sixty-hour weeks at the electronic parts distribution company he started. As a man of his generation, my father knew only one way to manage his stress—hit the gin.

Like her parents, my mother presented a front of composure and stability, even when her depressions were so debilitating she couldn't get out of bed. My father had no way of supporting her emotionally. She displayed a Kennedyesque image of our family of six: good looking, smart, talented, and a model for the community. We were the picture-perfect postcard of enviable health and promise. She never let anyone know she was depressed. She never told any of her friends about her condition. She never revealed it to her own parents and siblings. She had no therapists, no women's circles, no models for sharing emotional depth. So she "soldiered on," as she would say, ever the proud stoic. This standard made her appear brittle and unapproachable to me, especially on matters of the heart.

Although we rarely shared feelings in our family, my mother was always concerned when any of us were sick. In retrospect, understanding more about her personal history with mental illness, I imagine she must have been distraught when she heard about my struggle with depression. She feared the worst, that she had passed on to me the gene that had taken her and her father down. She made the trip to Providence and took me out to lunch for a rare one-on-one conversation. I made sure we went to a restaurant far from campus where none of my friends would see us. She asked about my mental state.

"How are you feeling?"

"I don't know."

"Are you depressed?"

"Well, I can't get out of bed. What would *you* call it?" I could hear the sarcasm in my voice. A chronic, as yet unexamined anger toward my mom seethed below the surface. It came out in curt, passive-aggressive answers to her questions. I was mad for many reasons I'd not yet worked through: her absence from my life due to her depressions, her inability to stop my dad's drinking and rage-alcoholism, her lack of emotional availability, her focus on appearance and elegance over emotional honesty, and her tendency toward quick judgment and dismissal of people she deemed below her social and academic class.

But in this moment, I saw the pain in her eyes as she ignored the sarcasm and pronounced, with sadness and resignation, "I'm afraid you've got the family disease. You know, your grandfather had it too."

I felt tension in my neck and heat rising in my throat. "Just because you're chronically depressed doesn't mean I'm going to be. I'm *nothing* like you, Mom. You've always acquiesced to those arrogant Harvard doctors and their damn smug diagnoses. But that's not me!"

I wanted no part of that diagnosis. I would not surrender to it. I would fight it with every ounce of my being. I would not share my mother's fate. Hadn't I done everything—sports, math, science, adventure, persistence, discipline—to follow the positive parts of my dad's trajectory?

This was 1982, and with the dogmatic clarity of a twenty-one-year-old empowered by feminist theory, I believed my mother had been "had" by the male-dominated medical profession and profit-driven pharmaceutical industry. I judged that she'd not done enough of her own "work" to "cure" herself of the disease. She should have been in therapy, confronted her raging husband, exercised more, eaten right. If she'd done all these things, I reasoned, she wouldn't need lithium or any other drugs. They were a crutch, and I wanted no part of them. The "family disease" was a myth of convenience for my mother's laziness. I was stronger than that. I would find my own way to a cure.

And so began my valiant, passionate, persistent-beyond-reason pursuit to conquer my depression. If it was Everest, I would climb it; if it was the moon, I would reach it; if it was fascism, I would defeat it. I would do anything to prove that I alone was in control of my life.

It would take me twenty-five years to discover the futility of this quest.

CHAPTER II

ROLLER-COASTER
TWENTIES

I managed to have enough credits to graduate, but the darkness did not lift. I walked through the graduation ceremony in my black cap and gown, surrounded by gleeful friends popping bottles of champagne and spraying each other. I felt no joy. I knew that I was missing the heart of a grand occasion. But I was numb, distant, disconnected from the emotion of the moment. It was as if there was an impenetrable wall between my friends and me. I felt isolated, unable to touch or be moved by the celebrations. And no matter how much my friends wanted to help, they had no power to pierce that bubble.

Having never experienced depression before, I had no idea when, if, or how I would emerge to rejoin life. I had been accepted to medical school and was supposed to start in the fall, three months later. The thought of going to school again terrified me.

I couldn't focus my brain on anything. I knew I wouldn't be able to do the work.

In June of 1982, just after the numbing graduation, some friends dragged me to a No Nukes rally in New York City. There were some two million people there. I stumbled onto a classmate named Marcie Brown, who was getting ready to go to Israel for a year-long Peace Corps-like program called "Sherut La'am—Service to the People." Marcie had been to the Holy Land before. She knew I'd been a religion major at Brown and that I was Jewish.

I didn't have the foresight during this depression to think about food or to figure out how to pack it. It was hard enough to get dressed and get my body to the No Nukes rally at Central Park. But my friends who'd brought blankets and a picnic lunch found us an empty stretch of grass. Marcie plopped down, her curly brown hair flying. She bit a large chunk out of an apple. "You should come with me," she said, chewing loudly. "Israel will blow your mind with its beauty. It's a place to heal. I'll see if there's room for you in Sherut La'am."

I'd been sick with depression for six months. Therapy, sports, friends, counseling—nothing had worked. The days had dragged on with endless cruelty. I had to try something. "If you can find me a way in, I'll go."

Two weeks later, I was sitting next to Marcie on a plane to Tel Aviv.

Something happened when my feet hit the ground in Israel. The Mediterranean light, the promise of something new, the stunningly beautiful faces, the history of my people, the romantic rhythm of the language, the steady structure of our days of study and work, the community of thirty other young people my age, the adventure of being ten thousand miles away from home for the first time, or simple coincidence. Whatever it was, my depression lightened as I walked down the airplane's stairs and jumped onto the tarmac with both feet.

Over the next several weeks I slowly began to feel my life again. I went running in the mornings and swimming in the Galilee in the afternoons. I was learning Hebrew for the first time, could follow the teacher, and was at the top of the class. My memory was back. At campfires by the sea, I felt my laughter emerge with ease. I mean this quite viscerally. I felt the joy of that laughter in my muscles and cells. I could read maps in Hebrew and lead my friends in adventures hitchhiking around the country, down to Jerusalem, to the Mediterranean coast, to the Dead Sea.

I found Israeli men exquisitely sexy, and because this was life before HIV, I had a good time enjoying them. By September, I realized with tremendous relief and gratitude that I was fully "back." My spiritual leanings and youthful idealism led me to believe that this land was, indeed, "holy." It had cured me.

Even when the sirens went off and bombs were dropped from southern Lebanon onto our village in northern Galilee and our teachers and guides shuttled us with the efficiency born of experience into a bomb shelter, ironically, I felt little fear. In classic Israeli pioneering tradition, we sang songs of courage and freedom to pass the time. I was not alone, and the experience of having company through a struggle was a relief. Spending that first week in a bomb shelter due to the 1982 Lebanon War didn't faze me. With my brain and humor mysteriously returned to me, a bomb shelter seemed like a Caribbean vacation compared with the hell I'd been living in.

Israel in the early 1980s was a place of magic, adventure, and idealism. This was before the intifada. It was still safe for a twenty-one-year-old to hitchhike around the country with her friends. Marcie and our new friends, Heidi, Sally, Hilary, Neil, and David climbed the ancient ruins of Masada at dawn and watched the sun emerge over the Jordanian mountains and the Dead Sea. We climbed the hills in Golan and the mountains overlooking the Galilee, where Jesus was said to have given "The Sermon on the Mount." We walked the ancient walls of Jerusalem, bombarded by the cacophony of sound and language that was the Arab quarter of the Old City, with its smell of fresh baked pita, halvah, and baklava.

We climbed the Mount of Olives and watched the sunset over the Golden Dome of the Rock in Jerusalem: The rock Jews claimed as the place where the angels came to Abraham and told him to spare his son Isaac, and where Muslims built their magnificent golden mosque above the Western Wall of the Temple of King Solomon, claiming it as holy ground. The combination of people, land, history, and adventure were intoxicating. I started crafting a sense of identity as a woman of the Hebrew tribe. And there was something else: Yitzhak and Iftach and Pesach and Noam, the dark-skinned, curly-haired Israeli men, each more gorgeous to my eyes than the next.

I worked on a fish farm at the most southern tip of Israel on the Red Sea, where two of the Earth's tectonic plates meet. The power of that collision gave birth to towering mountains in Jordan to the east and Israel to the west. From the farm, I had a view of the biblical Mount Nebo, where Moses was said to have laid eyes on the Promised Land but was not allowed to enter.

Noam, a lead scientist in the research lab attached to the farm, and I slept under the stars by his cabin on the beach. He had an old wooden sailboat and an array of fishing gear. At dawn he'd strap a knife to his ankle, grab his snorkel, and dive into the surf, emerging fifteen minutes later with breakfast: the Red Sea catch of the day. Inspired, I learned to dive too.

In the daytime, the pink corals look like funny shaped rocks. But at night (picture the movie *Fantasia*) they come alive, swaying with the rhythm of the sea. "Fish" seems too common a term to describe the rainbow-colored swimming creatures that populate this sea. I think the Creator must have had an exquisite day when coming up with this expanse. There were angel fish that swelled up like balloons, exposing deadly needles; corals of pink and gold that seemed to dance with the current to Mozart; and sting rays shaped like the Starship Enterprise—all of this sea life moving to a mysterious rhythm of grace and flow.

Under the stars, Noam took me to his favorite coral reefs for a dive. In the eternal silence of the nighttime sea, we swam hand in hand, watching corals come alive, swaying to a silent beat. Noam, who had been raised in these waters, moved as if one with the undersea beings. Swimming alongside him, I felt my heart buzzing to this rare adventure.

Noam did the job of four people. He was responsible for breeding tilapia, counting larvae, tracking water pressure, salinity, and temperature, and seemingly loving up each and every fish at the aquaculture lab where we worked. At lunch, the twenty of us lab workers ate together outside, always sharing food. Noam would peel an orange and give everyone a slice, waiting until everyone else was fed before he took his own. He brought dark chocolate and fresh tomatoes from the Kibbutz so sweet and juicy that we ate them like fruit. I'd never met an American man like Noam. I'd never met anyone like him.

My brother Dan called and said he was getting married to his college girlfriend, a brilliant, blond cheerleader from Montana. I was so in love with Noam, how could I leave now? But in our family the expectations were clear. There was no question that I would be at Dan's wedding.

I held on with all my heart to Noam as we said our goodbye. The word in Hebrew is *"l'hitraot,"* which translates roughly as, "I'll see you soon." I knew I'd be back. I just didn't know how or when. So just shy of one year in Israel, I left my Mediterranean paradise in late May and flew home to Massachusetts for the wedding and then, according to plan, to attend Dartmouth Medical School in September.

Ronald Reagan was president, the "me generation" and Wall Street traders were king. The imposing buildings and Ivy traditions of Dartmouth sucked the life out of my soul. And, as if the "demons" resided only in New England, my depression returned with a vengeance. I dropped out of med school within two weeks. I didn't want to leave, but I couldn't focus on more than a paragraph in an anatomy textbook. My academic discipline evaporated; once again, I had no capacity to retain data. My brain could not make simple calculations. Sentences blurred on the page. I could not absorb concepts in anatomy and physiology. A consummate navigator in Israel, I could barely find my way around campus. The darkness was back. I was petrified.

When I was 23, I returned to Israel in pursuit of a geographical cure. This worked for a time, prompting me to believe that this was indeed Divine country and I'd been called there. Then, the depression hit again when I was living in Tel Aviv. Through the distorted, chronically negative eye of the depressive, I concluded that "Israel as the Divine country" had been a fantasy. I couldn't feel or remember the gifts from Noam or remember the majesty of the Red Sea. I wandered the streets of the city without bearing or focus. Feeling completely alone and too far from home, I got on a plane to Boston.

I spent the rest of my twenties alternating between six months of debilitating depression and six months of relative clarity and energy. At twenty-eight, I was living in Boston and in full-on depression. I had just dropped out of another grad school, this one the Kennedy School of Government at Harvard. Friends who knew I liked to be outdoors learned of a marketing job at a retreat center being built in the Berkshire hills of Western Massachusetts, which seemed to fit my qualifications. I somehow managed to get through the interview and land the job. Though I was afraid I wouldn't be able to make it away from friends and family, I figured I had little to lose, since the isolated life of winter in the city exacerbated my pain. Maybe the "geographical cure" could work again, as it had in Israel. I moved to the Berkshires.

This proved an elixir for my soul: the beauty of the land, the easy access to physical exertion in nature, the yoga practice I learned from my roommate, who studied at the local ashram, the healthy eating I picked up from the abundance of local macrobiotics. This was followed by a move to the University of Massachusetts for grad school, studying for an MBA. There, I landed among a community of wonderful kindred spirits—progressive, outdoorsy, warm, loving friends.

I lucked into fabulous work in my chosen field—organizational development—with the acknowledged world leader in the work, and through that network, met a guy from Milwaukee named Joe.

CHAPTER III

SOUL WORK

By all logic, it couldn't work. I built a well-reasoned, brick-walled defense: Joe was too old, too divorced, too white, too antifeminist, too into shooting deer and turkeys, for my vegetarian sensibilities. We lived 1,800 miles apart. I wanted to get married. He was separated but not yet divorced from his second wife. I wanted kids, and he already had three—plus a vasectomy. I wanted to live a Jewish life, and he was raised Catholic. I wanted to live in Western Massachusetts, and he had spent his forty-one years in Milwaukee. I worked during the week as a business consultant; he worked weekends doing men's personal growth workshops. I did all the calculations. There was no possible way that this could work. So I let my guard down.

When Joe sent me a handwritten letter that he wanted to visit me for a weekend in Massachusetts because he believed we had "soul work" to do together, I thought that was the smoothest New

Age pick-up line I'd heard yet. But I also thought it was creative, so I consented with this caveat: No sex.

"I'm involved with two men right now, and that's already a mess, so I want to be clear," I announced to Joe over the phone. "Your visit has to be strictly platonic." I was proud of my forthrightness.

"No problem," Joe said, in a voice that conveyed calm and connection. "I'll just be happy to see you again." He sounded like he meant it.

Joe's soulfulness was not unexpected, considering how we'd met. I'd been invited to participate in a professional growth workshop known as Shadow Work®, north of Boston, along with several colleagues from the MIT Organizational Learning Center where I got a job out of Grad School. The seminar was designed to improve our skills as facilitators and leaders of groups in business organizations. Twenty-eight people would be participating. I knew that Shadow Work was based on Swiss psychiatrist Dr. Carl Jung's concept of the shadow self; I had written a paper on this in grad school the year before.

Jung's idea was that the Shadow is the part of our psyche we repress, deny, and disown. He wrote, "To confront a person with his own shadow is to show him his own light." A colleague I admired said that Shadow Work was the most powerful personal growth experience he'd ever had, and he'd had many. When I asked what to expect, he said, with Oxford-trained understatement, "Healing, I suspect." As the date approached, I had an instinct that something powerful was about to happen.

It turned out that Shadow Work's founder, Cliff Barry, was Joe's best friend. Cliff invited Joe to witness Shadow Work, an evolution of their work together, when he brought it to the East

Coast for the first time. Joe looked at his calendar, realized he'd be in DC that weekend, and said, "Sure. I have to come East anyway." It would be his first time setting foot in Massachusetts. Little did he know, he wasn't leaving.

I was a thirty-two-year-old with an MBA from UMass and a consulting job based out of MIT with one of the hottest management gurus in the country. I'd had lovers, been an instructor for Outward Bound, part of Sherut La'am, and had even done three months of basic training in the Israeli Army, in a program reserved for non-Israeli youths. I had a thirty-something "happening" social life and kept friends from kindergarten through grad school. My work took me across the country and back and allowed me to connect with some of the most brilliant minds in my field. Life was full and rich. I'd bought a new hunter green Jeep Cherokee, debt-free, with all-wheel drive to negotiate the mountainous, icy dirt roads in the rural town where I lived. My dark days of depression were a thing of the past—I hadn't been down in four years. I thought I'd licked them through personal discipline and sheer will, and they weren't coming back. There was only one thing missing: a life partner.

On the opening day of the three-day workshop, held in a quaint fishing town north of Boston, the scent of snow was in the air. It was cozy to sit inside by the hearth in a circle with twenty-eight colleagues and friends. I scanned the room and saw a man sitting cross-legged, wearing a logging shirt. Broad-shouldered and thick-haired, with a rich brown beard, he seemed exquisitely comfortable in his body. There was something familiar about him. When he spoke, I thought, "I could listen to that voice for a long time." His was a chocolaty baritone, projecting with ease across the room, warm in tone, with a slight accent that said he was not from Boston.

Later he told me he'd been smitten when he first heard me speak across the circle. "Something about your voice told me, 'I want to know that woman.'"

A soft snow was falling that March equinox night, and I wanted to go for a walk outside and feel the snowflakes on my face. I had the sense I'd like to go with someone, but I didn't know who. As I was putting my boots on, Joe appeared. "Do you want to go for a walk in the snow?" he asked, reading my mind.

I remember a golden glow in the air that night. We walked along a tree-lined rural road sharing stories of the outdoors and family and politics and spirit. I had the eerie yet comforting feeling that I'd known Joe for a long time. When it was time to go inside, we both had the instinct to assault the innocent hot tubbers with snowballs. Earlier in the day, I'd found myself giving the keys to my brand-new Jeep to Joe when he needed to run an errand for Cliff in the snow. "Better go in the AWD for safety," I'd said as I handed over my prized possession. What in the world made me let this perfect stranger drive my car? Why was I treating him like family?

The last morning, when my chance came to do a piece of Shadow Work, I leapt at it. The facilitators, Cliff Barry and Mary Ellen Blandford, had shown themselves to be consummate healers, working with two people before me. One woman was a survivor of repeated incest. Another was a single mother whose parents kicked her out when they discovered she was pregnant at seventeen. Cliff and Mary Ellen were insightful, compassionate, focused, and full of blessings for these two.

Somehow it appeared to me that each of these women had been transformed through the alchemy of Shadow Work. They glowed. I felt confident that I was in exceptionally good hands. Cliff and Mary Ellen asked their opening question: "What do you want to have happen here?" I replied by naming my most persistent desire: "I want to find my ideal lover."

Cliff asked me to choose someone to play the dramatized role of that lover. I'd thoroughly enjoyed walking in the woods with Joe the night before—the choice was obvious. "Joe, would you do that for me?"

"I'd be delighted to," he answered, rising to his feet.

Ninety minutes later, after an epic saga of slaying inner dragons and all other obstacles, the heroine (me) finally got to stand face-to-face with her long-awaited lover (Joe). The crowd cheered as we embraced.

Then Joe replied, ad-libbing his lines for the first time: "From now on, honey, it's whatever you want, whenever you want, for as long as you want." Our friends who witnessed this scene later reported, "You guys thought that was theatre; we knew it was real."

Ten weeks later, on Memorial Day weekend, Joe flew in to visit me for our "soul work" date. I knew he'd separated from his wife the year before and was living on his own, dating several women. I felt safe in my espoused desire to just be friends. I was happy to pick him up at the airport in my favorite spring-has-finally-arrived-in-New-England flower print dress. And despite my insistence on a platonic connection, I was surprised at my delight in seeing him. It was like welcoming a long-lost lover home.

We arrived at my place in the woods late in the evening, settled in, and lit a fire that flickered off the wood floor and warmed his face. He had brought me a gift.

"I shot this myself," he said, "in the woods of northern Minnesota," and then presented me, the devoted vegetarian, with a deerskin.

"Thanks, Joe," I said, stunned by the dead animal remains, but wanting to be gracious. Then I touched the contours of the skin and snuggled it against my cheek, feeling its velvety softness.

"Here," he gestured, lying down on the skin by the fire. "It's cozy."

We lay there for a while, sipping tea and talking. Joe was in a sober mood. One of his closest friends and mentors had just been shot in a grisly murder-suicide. "Ron spoke of tomorrow like he had it in his shirt pocket. We never do. At his funeral three women showed up, each believing she was the one. When I go, I want everyone to know that there was only one woman for Joe Laur."

Soon, it was late and time to suggest sleeping arrangements.

"I'm going to head up to bed. You can have the couch here, the futon in the sunroom, or you can join me in my room." (Joe loves to retell this part of the story.) "Which would you pick?"

His choice was obvious and my solid commitment to a platonic friendship melted in about five minutes of snuggling up to this muscled, solid, warm man. It was Memorial Day weekend, hereafter "Meltmorial" in our lexicon.

We spent our time the next day hiking the state forests near home. Joe was exceedingly comfortable in the woods, delighting the Outward Bound instructor in me. He wasn't so great at planting my spring garden, but hey, hunters aren't usually great gatherers. He knew every Beatles song and sang in harmony in my key. And when it was time to run errands, the guy brought a poetry book and read me Rumi from the passenger seat.

On Sunday morning, relaxing with hot tea and the *New York Times* in my sunroom, I was sprawled on the futon and Joe was sitting on the floor next to me with his head against my belly. I scratched the place where his hairline met his neck, and he nuzzled up to my hand like a puppy. He kissed me and we made love. I was moved to tears. I'd never felt this seen and safe with a man before.

Then I got angry at myself. I remembered the promise I'd made in a self-induced confessional a few weeks prior after a couple of disastrous affairs: that the next guy I made love with I would marry. I knew that could not possibly be Joe. The logistics were impossible.

When Joe flew home the next day, I had to bite my lip to keep from crying. Must be the oxytocin, I reasoned later, recalling the hormone that women release when we nurse and make love. Makes you sentimental. "I'll get over it," I thought.

But I did not. And found that every rendezvous we had in the next nine months, anywhere our schedules coincided—San Francisco in June, Cape Cod in August, Santa Fe in September, home for my thirty-third birthday in November, to Joe's cabin in northern Minnesota in December (with the wind-chill minus sixty)—removed a few more bricks from the Great Wall around my heart.

Joe moved east to live with me after a year and half and we were married on a glorious crisp Cape Cod day a year after that. For the next several years, we lived a pretty idyllic existence. We founded Seed Systems, a lucrative consulting business that took us all over the world; built a house on sixteen acres by a stream; and lived in an extended community of loving friends and colleagues. I had the energy to carry it all with grace and gratitude. Given the pattern of my twenties, I was convinced I'd licked my depression myself—just as I'd known I would. Unlike my mother, I was a winner, someone who could will herself to health, beauty, success, and love.

Until it all came crashing down, when I fell thirty feet off a mountain ravine in Mexico, barely escaping with my life.

CHAPTER IV

AFTER THE FALL

When my friends Puja and Patricia organized a yoga and writing retreat for women just south of Puerto Vallarta, Mexico, I jumped. The seaside village of Yelapa is an indigenous community, accessible only by boat, with no cars and no electricity. I'd heard you could walk through town on paths shared with donkeys, schoolchildren, and the occasional bicycle. As I cleared snow from our monstrously steep, icy driveway for what seemed like the hundredth time that February, I counted the days until departure.

On our third day in Yelapa, I was dressed in my favorite outdoor attire: shorts, bathing suit, shirt, water shoes, baseball cap, and shades. I hiked up a trail, looking for a series of waterfalls I'd been shown the day before by a local teenage guide and had located on a topographical map.

I led my hiking buddy to the first waterfall, and we plunged our shoulders under the rushing stream, sun-drenched, wedged between two rocks, singing. I wanted every woman there to share this peak experience. One by one, as they arrived, I showed them how to hold me by the wrist for the best grip. As I pulled them into the safe spot between the rocks with water rushing over their shoulders and sun in their hair, they beamed.

"Alisa, do you want to go to the upper waterfall?" I asked. Puja and I had been to this glorious spot the day before with our eleven-year-old local guide, and I was pretty sure I could retrace his steps.

"Sure," she agreed. We left the pack behind, splashing in the water.

Energized from the natural Jacuzzi, I set a moderately fast pace up a steep incline. Before I realized it, I was off the trail and on some loose gravel at about a forty-five-degree pitch, not knowing where I was. My footing was not good, and I could feel my heart pounding. Breathe. Slow down. Get your bearings.

"Sara, come down from there!" Alisa shouted with alarm. I made it off the steep incline and felt somewhat relieved. Still, the waterfall we'd bathed in was rushing just below us and the rocky soil under our feet was loose. I knew we were in a precarious position.

"Let's backtrack and see if we can rejoin the lower trail," I suggested. I headed back down the incline gingerly. To my surprise—I had won a navigation award in the Israeli Army—I couldn't find it. I experienced a bit of vertigo at this. Then Alisa exclaimed,

"It's here. I'm on it!"

I took one step in her direction. She was on the trail, two paces from me. How did I miss it? With one more step onto a flat, solid boulder about six feet wide, I'd join her there.

I took that step, and my weight alone dislodged the boulder from its cliff-side perch. Suddenly, I was tumbling limb over limb, bouncing off jagged-edged rocks. My descent was accelerating. Having been here two days prior, I knew there was nothing to break my fall. With that realization came the horrible thought that I would die, with a thud and a snap, at the bottom of the cliff in the rocky arroyo below. I screamed my desperation, *Noooooo!*

No! You are not letting me die here, in an arroyo three thousand miles from Joe and home, at the tender age of thirty-eight, in my prime, yet still childless. NOOOO, this is NOT the way it ends.

At the final precipice, ten feet above the arroyo, a small tree, no more than an inch in diameter, broke my fall, catching me on a shelf only as wide as my hips. Terror shifted to awe, in a moment's awareness that I hadn't died. I felt an egg-sized protrusion on the left side of my forehead, saw the blood oozing from gashes on all limbs, felt a searing pain in my chest, where I'd been struck by the boulder, yet I was conscious. Breathing. Alive.

Like a mom who lifts a car from her child in superhuman strength, Puja leapt the ten feet from the rocks below to my side in one stride. She put her hand on my heart and held me. Immediately, I began to sob from shock, pain, and relief. Alisa, still perched on the trail above, was at my side in equally record time. She swore that the tree had not been there on our ascent. "The angels must have sent it."

We were about four miles upstream on a rough trail the women of the writing retreat had taken. Half of us had traveled by foot and half on horseback. Someone gladly surrendered her horse to me, and four women hoisted me up into the saddle. I could not sit, but I could wrap my arms around the muscled neck of my equestrian savior, a placid, surefooted soul named "Colorado." I remember being simultaneously in excruciating pain and sheer awe at the vivid beauty of the mountains against azure sky as Colorado shuffled me down the hillside, step by step.

I was alive.

Back at our hotel, a place not incidentally called "Casa Milagros" (House of Miracles), the women crafted an outdoor operating table for me out of a massage table and white sheet. Pavarti, a doctor, spoke first. "You've got abrasions on 80 percent of your body and flesh wounds just below both knees, the left shoulder, right thigh, back, and head."

Relieved to be receiving medical attention, I was also fearful at my prospects for recovery. Were there internal injuries to lungs or spleen? Blood loss, concussion? In a remote Mexican village far from hospital, drugs, or electricity, how would I heal? Celia, the only nurse in a village of 1,500, began to clean my flesh wounds. She gave me a tetanus shot and antibiotics. My breathing and heart calmed, and I felt grateful for the gentle, skillful care of these women as they cleaned and bandaged me.

The next day, I felt sore in every crevice; battered and beaten. I couldn't lift my left arm above shoulder level, and it hurt to breathe, perhaps due to broken ribs. Alisa, who had been there the day I met Joe, offered to call him.

"We've got to let Joe know what's happened and that you're all right."

"No way."

"Why not, Honey? He needs to know."

"Alisa, you know Joe. When you go to the phone and explain to him that I've fallen forty feet off a cliff, nearly died, am in a village with no medical center, can't come to the phone, but am healing just fine, he'll go ballistic. He'll be on the next plane. I think I'll heal best by being here and resting in the warmth of the sun until Sunday."

The imprint of the fall was all over my body, but a few days later, as I waited for my reunion with Joe at the Boston airport (he was coincidentally flying in from work in another city) I was once again dressed for winter. Only the flesh on my hands and face was exposed. I wanted to tell him right away, but our ever-reliable friend Patty was there to pick us up, right on time, and I wanted to wait until we were alone. Joe and I embraced, kissed, held each other. Me with utter gratitude, Joe still unaware that this reunion at baggage claim was any different than countless others we'd had before.

Patty helped us get our bags in the car, and I went to sit in the passenger seat of her new AWD RAV4. Joe got in back and held my hand.

"Honey, what did you do to your hand? You've got a serious gash here."

If only he knew.

"I fell," I said in my most understated tone, holding my breath. Not yet. I wanted to be alone with him in our home when I told him.

When we were a few miles from home, it began to snow, and the rural roads were slick. On one rise, we skidded, and the car did a 180, heading for the steep precipice on the north side of the road. I've lived in New England my whole life and am used to winter skids. This time, I gasped and winced.

"Hey, it's cool Sara," Patty said, almost defensively. "Just a little skid. I'll have you home in a minute."

She couldn't imagine my terror at careening toward a cliff.

We got home. Turned on the lights. Unloaded our gear and lit a fire in the wood stove. Our winter reentry ritual. Taking a full breath, I turned to Joe.

"I have something to tell you. But I think it's best if I show you."

I began to take my clothes off. Layer by layer until I reached the flesh. I watched Joe's eyes widen, then glisten. "What happened, Honey?" he said, holding me close. I was uncharacteristically at a loss for words. "I was on a hike, and I fell. . . ." I tried to describe the indescribable. "When I knew I would die, I bargained with G-d. 'No. I cannot leave Joe here and die at the bottom of this arroyo! This is not how it's going to end.' I felt like it was the angels of our future babies who caught me on the edge of that precipice."

I slid down my pants to show him the place by my right hip where the tree had broken my fall.

"Can you see that?" I asked.

"There's a bruise there." he said. "It looks like someone's handprint on your pelvis."

"That's exactly what I thought. Do you think angels have hands?"

Though I felt awe and gratitude that I'd been snatched from death, my relief at being alive gave way in short order to a gnawing sense of anxiety. It was as if the flesh wounds in my chest between my breasts had seared into my heart. My constitutional physical fearlessness was replaced by an unfamiliar unease in my body when outdoors. There is a narrow log we use to cross the stream below our house that I usually traverse without a second thought.

Now the sight of it, with water rushing below, brought tears to my eyes and involuntary shaking to my limbs. I'd always relied on the infallibility of my body, but the encounter with mortality on the Mexican mountain left me in terror. The earth had been swept from beneath my feet, and I was shaken to my foundation.

The physical trauma and psychological horror of the fall triggered cascades of terror throughout my being—emotionally, mentally, and spiritually. A dreaded sensation that I'd not experienced for more than a decade flooded me: the sense that I was falling uncontrollably into the abyss that was my personal experience of depression. This time, there was no miracle tree to stop me, no circle of women healers to nurse me back to health.

And though I'd been thoroughly convinced that it would never happen, I found myself sucked down into a vortex, down into the underworld, once again at the mercy of my demons.

CHAPTER V

THREE STRIKES AND I'M OUT

I am nothing like my mother—I am a big achiever. I excel at math and sports and friends. I am a serious competitor and have no patience for people who can't keep up. Teachers and coaches smile on me. Despite the fact that I love math, my favorite high school teacher is the English teacher Margaret Metzger. I love her because she is young and feisty. She is the only adult I know who asks questions with genuine curiosity and encourages us to write and talk about taboo subjects like sex and romance and religion and politics. Mrs. Metzger says to me, "Sara, everything you touch turns to gold." She muses that my parents must be stellar. I don't reveal the truth about my home life, that my father, though a handsome, successful CEO, is an alcoholic, and my mother was so depressed during my early childhood that she stayed in bed for weeks at a time. I just smile.

Actually, my mother is doing well these days. She finished her degree and is working part-time as a geriatric social worker. She and my father look dazzling again, all glitter and gold when they go out on the town. She is witty and engaging in conversations with friends. She writes letters to the editor of the Boston Globe on progressive causes, and they get published. She is the attractive Wellesley College intellect once again, and she revels in it.

One day after hockey practice, I use the shower in my parents' bathroom because the water pressure there is better. I find my mother's new pills on the sink. The bottle is wide and clear this time and the prescription says "lithium."

I call to her, "What are these for, Mom?"

"Oh, that's just something I take to keep me from getting depressed."

Maybe these are why she's healthy. My feelings about my mother's depressions are confused. When it comes time to write a high school senior honors paper for Madeline Morris's class, I decide to do some research into what this "lithium" is for. I learn that lithium works for people with manic depression disease, and conversely, if lithium works for you, that is diagnostic of being a manic-depressive. I report this to Mom one afternoon, thinking this will be of some comfort. There is a name for what she has and a cure.

"Mom, the scientists have proven that if lithium is a cure for your depression, that means you have manic depression."

I think this is pretty cool—to have a definition and a cure. But my mom takes the label as an accusation.

"I am NOT manic and definitely DON'T have manic depression." Her face gets tight; she is emphatic. There is no room to argue with this tone. I get that she accepts the idea of her clinical depression, yet not the stigma of insanity that goes with the term "manic." I agree: she's never shown any signs of mania. I wonder why lithium works.

"Mom, when did you start taking these things?

"Since you were about fifteen."

That must explain why she's been well since then.

"How does it work?"

"No one seems to know. But thank goodness it does."

I begin to put some pieces together. I realize that when she is on lithium, she is stable, happy, capable; without it, she is a train wreck. When she felt fine, she reasoned she didn't need the medicine anymore. It might have long-term side effects, and who wants to take pills anyway? So she'd take herself off it, and begin a rapid free fall to mental catastrophe and inability to function.

Our first open conversations about our family history of depression follow. I am almost off to college—she must think I'm old enough to know. I knew my grandfather, her father, Lewis, had been a pillar in his community, president of his company, president of his synagogue and chairman of numerous charities in the proud New England city of Worcester. He was the father of three accomplished children and ten grandchildren, several Ivy Leaguers among them. An immigrant's son, he had gone to Harvard on scholarship when the university still maintained a quota for Jews. But he had been in the depths of a cruel depression when he died of cancer in his early eighties, leaving this world with a self-assessment painfully distorted by the disease, believing that his life had been worthless.

"Mom, what happened to Grandpa?"

I knew he'd been through electric shock in the 1950s. But families didn't talk about these things then. Appearances were kept up and the illusion of his invulnerability had been carefully maintained.

"He had a devastating depression after your aunt and uncle and I were grown." My mom looked off into the distance, sadness in her voice. "Electric shock was the treatment of choice at the time. It was horrible, but it gave him his life back."

"So he suffered with depression even back then? Not just recently?"

"Yes, I'm sorry to say. He had the family disease."

A sense of terror and helplessness resided in my cells after the fall, exacerbated by my grief at our inability to conceive. Nearing forty, I felt the longing in my womb for children, whom I'd already named Sam and Maya. Joe had had a vasectomy before we met, but with characteristic optimism, I'd believed that we could reverse that, no problem. By the time of my fall, we'd had one failed attempt at reversing it and were seeking out another doctor. It had proved more difficult than we'd anticipated, and tension was mounting.

"You've already got three biological kids that you love, Joe. We have great relationships with them. What does it matter if we just go to the bank and get some healthy sperm?"

"No, I couldn't do that."

"Why not? What difference does it make?" I was incredulous at Joe's selfishness, blocking me from conceiving *my* children.

"I know it's not rational, but I'm afraid I won't love them like my own."

"Oh, come on. You know what that means you're asking me to do? Do you know the alternative? It's more hormones and chemicals and shots for my body."

"I'll find another surgeon. There's got to be someone who can reverse this thing."

I felt a gnawing sense that time was slipping by, Joe and I were at an impasse, and I might lose my chance to have my own children, nurse them, raise them. My heart ached.

As if these two challenges, my fall and the infertility, were not enough, in early 1999 a third trial arose, this one professional.

Joe and I were working on the business we'd cofounded, "Seed Systems." Seed's purpose was to create green businesses and jobs, and I must say, from the vantage point of two decades later in 2020, with the rise in climate change awareness, we were well ahead of our time with Seed's vision.

One of the world's largest and most revered sports multinational corporations, a company I'll call "4T," had hired us for an unprecedented project. They wanted us to create a leadership training program that would transform their culture of twenty thousand employees into a place dedicated to the Triple Bottom Line of business: people, profit, and planet. 4T had announced dramatic internal goals for manufacturing that were unheard of at the time—zero waste, zero toxic chemicals, 100 percent recyclable, 100 percent remanufacturable.

We were eager to design and lead what amounted to a year-long executive graduate school experience. Participants would gain skills and knowledge in ecological sustainability and executive leadership and apply these to their business projects: for example, recyclable shirts and compostable shoes that would make new environmental theories practical for business.

The design team, consisting of Joe and me, along with partners at 4T, worked beautifully together. It looked like stars were aligning for a big success. Then it happened—the feeling of accelerating into an invisible brick wall as it simultaneously accelerates toward you. Perhaps this sensation was a psychic repeat of the terror of the fall.

I don't know exactly when or how, but suddenly our goodwill at 4T evaporated like so much water in the desert in July. No oasis to be found. Our tried-and-true tools and tricks, accumulated from years of consulting, facilitating, teaching, and coaching, fell flat. Work that had won us professional respect and appreciation in other settings was suddenly viewed at 4T as cliché, elitist, irrelevant—or worse.

At one point, my salt-of-the-earth, heartland-raised Joe had a new pair of reading glasses. Unaccustomed to wearing these, he had placed them on top of his head. The 4T audience of 350 commented in their written critiques of the day that Joe, my Midwestern hunter guy, was an "Arrogant East Coaster" because of how he wore his glasses. My comments about the heart and soul underlying sustainability in business were reviewed as "touchy-feely" and soft. And our style of asking questions and encouraging inquiry, as opposed to lecturing with the "right" answers, was seen as lacking content expertise. The rumors spread that Schley and Laur did not fit 4T culture. This reputation followed us for the next fifteen months as we lived out the painful terms of our contract. Never had I had a professional experience that was so disheartening, frustrating, and humbling.

Despite the harsh treatment, I couldn't figure out why 4T's hooks sunk so deep in me. While Joe wasn't thrilled with the experience, he seemed to let the client's critiques slide off him like proverbial water off a duck's back. He'd ignore it and move on to his next project—building a sauna or hunting for deer or reading Rumi. But I felt shattered and exhausted. Working in corporate settings, I usually carried a thick skin that enabled me to survive, even thrive. I was an organizational healer, a coach, a mender of broken souls. This time, my soul had shattered like the poet Rolf Jacobsen's "Chrysanthemum" into a thousand pieces. And it seemed there was no one to put me back together. We had daily meetings with the client; I cringed at each one. I couldn't find my voice or my stride or my power or my gifts. And with the visceral memory of the fall off the mountain fresh in my bones, this lack of agency was terrifying.

Three strikes—the devastating fall, the unknowns of infertility, and the client from hell—and I was out, the stress proving more than my nervous system could bear. The old but painfully familiar pattern of brain dysfunction I hadn't experienced in more than a decade returned. I could not work, could not think, did not return friends' calls, could barely get myself dressed. These difficulties were more emotionally painful than before because my belief that I had licked this disease through superior will and discipline was blown apart. I began to doubt that any of my positive beliefs about myself were true. The painfully familiar sense of being at the mercy of some cruel mysterious force beyond my control was back, and I felt helpless to heal myself.

Joe felt helpless too. Although he'd heard me describe the depressions of my twenties, he'd never seen it live in me. It was as if his lover had been abducted to the underworld by an unseen force. He was a guy who prided himself on having the right tools to fix just about anything. Not this time.

Then, after an endless year of suffering, Juanita sent me a lifeline.

CHAPTER VI

JUANITA'S EMPATHY

Juanita, my mentor and friend, is a woman I admire for her professional savvy, smarts, and success. She'd heard through our grapevine that I was down with depression. To my surprise, she explained that she'd also suffered for years with it. She called from California. "Sara, you do not have to suffer. You've done nothing wrong. This is DNA, it's genetic, it's biochemical. If you had diabetes you'd take insulin. This is no different." I respected Juanita. I listened. I felt a wave of relief.

Juanita was taking Sam-e, a naturally occurring supplement that had been successfully used for depression in Europe. Sam-e had just become available in the US. She suggested I read *Stop Depression Now* by Dr. Richard Brown. A credentialed psycho-pharmacologist who taught at Columbia University, Dr. Brown reported that in double-blind clinical studies, Sam-e was found equally as effective in treating depression as Prozac, with none of the side effects of Prozac. I still wanted to be pregnant and was adamant that I would not take any pharmaceutical drugs for fear of their impact in utero. But my depression was increasingly debilitating, and I was grasping for a lifeline. Trusting Juanita, I opted to try Sam-e. I was thirty-nine years old, and this was the first time any medication for the disease had crossed my lips.

After three weeks on Sam-e, I found glimmers of life again. Color returned to my vision. I laughed at a few jokes. My colleagues at the 4T did not seem as difficult. And I made love with my husband with gratitude and joy for the first time in almost a year.

This stuff was a miracle, and I was grateful. I became an advocate and a resource for others, believing that not only had it saved me, but also as a naturally occurring substance, it could cause no harm to in-utero or nursing babies.

An extremely productive year followed. (Only later did I learn that for my bipolar brain, Sam-e acts like something between caffeine and cocaine. I was speeding but didn't know it.) I returned to healthy lifestyle habits: exercise, diet, yoga, as well as prayer, friends, community, and loving my man.

In that year we finished the contract with 4T and started a consortium of Fortune 500 businesses dedicated to sustainability. I went through professional training to be certified as a leader of ShadowWork. I also started writing again. (I'd had a few professional articles published before my fall.) Joe got his vasectomy successfully reversed, and I regained my faith that we would indeed have children.

Most of all, I was grateful for the day-to-day, with my brain restored to its "natural" functioning. The ability to accomplish simple tasks like sorting laundry, washing dishes, and putting away groceries seemed miraculous. I felt great joy in that. Spring had come to New England. Purple tulips were shooting up in our recently frozen ground, the days were lengthening, and the sun appeared once again on the horizon.

CHAPTER VII

TWICE BLESSED

The following April, after the close of our contract with the client from hell, feeling the energy of spring and new possibilities, I decided to take a class with Terri Nash, esteemed local wise woman, midwife, and homeopathic healer. Terri defied the stereotype of someone with those credentials. She had a Boston accent, a raucous laugh, and a compassion and wisdom born of overcoming serious personal challenges. I liked Terri immediately. Our shared history in Red Sox territory and our tendency toward wry wit made us fast friends. I shared my struggles with depression and dreams of mothering with Terri.

By that time, Joe and I had already failed at several alternative attempts to get pregnant, namely IUI (intrauterine insemination), the high-tech version of the "turkey baster" method.

"I used to think and feel I was impenetrable, unflappable, on top of the world," I told Terri. "No fears, a history of success, lots of joy, and freedom. Then I hit the wall."

She laughed with me.

"Here's how I see it," she said. "When we think we run the show, the universe comes along and whacks us with a small cast-iron pan on the side of our head. A brush with death, for example. If we don't get it that time, if we still think we're the Number One in control, the universe comes along with a bigger cast-iron pan. Still don't get it? The universe's cast-iron pans just keep getting bigger until we finally do get it."

I must have had a pretty good control addiction, as the universe was showing up with a series of increasingly heavier cast-iron pans.

Joe and I had been working with Cindy, a seasoned and compassionate nurse in Boston's leading IVF (in vitro fertilization) clinic. Cindy made it clear that our options were limited, given our failed attempts with lower-tech methodologies.

"Sara, you're a fit forty, but you're still forty. It's time you two do an IVF trial."

IVF would require me to inject drugs into my abdomen. Despite my aversion to chemical interventions, I finally agreed, understanding that this might be the last chance to get pregnant with Joe.

One of the IVF meds is FSH (Follicle Stimulating Hormone). Its purpose is to do just that, to trigger the ovaries to ovulate more eggs than the standard one per month. The more eggs that are released, the higher the chance one will become a viable embryo. Administering the drugs is a delicate balancing act: too little, and you won't release the eggs, too much, and the body can go into what's known as "ovarian hyperstimulation," a potentially life-threatening situation for the prospective mother.

Roll the dice, and that was me.

Two weeks into the protocol, I woke up to excruciating pain. I called Cindy in a panic, trying to stay calm as I said, "I feel like someone is torturing me in the abdomen. I can barely move from the pain. And the scale says I've gained five pounds. I think it's all water."

"Sara, get someone to drive you to Beth Israel, now." Our local hospitals were quite good, but not Boston caliber. I knew it must be serious if Cindy insisted I make the two-hour drive to the city.

I learned later that the thirty-some follicles the FSH had stimulated had produced an overdose of progesterone. As a result, my veins had become porous. Water was flowing out of them into what is known as "the third cavity"—the areas between organs. Counterintuitively, though I was rapidly gaining water weight, I was at risk of death by dehydration. My second brush with death in as many years. Bring on the cast-iron pans.

Once on intravenous fluids at the hospital, the danger of death by dehydration passed. But my formerly independent abdominal organs were now sloshing up against each other in an unnatural sea of water. The pain was excruciating. I could not walk to the bathroom. With my flesh puffed out from twenty pounds of extra water, I looked like an ancient elephant. Imagine what your fingers look like after a long soak in the tub. Now expand that vision to cover your entire body. The doctors making their rounds didn't seem to have a plan to address this. Barely able to sit up, I called Cindy. "Is this normal?"

"I'm so sorry, you're the one in a thousand who gets ovarian hyperstimulation from IVF. We do see this occasionally. The pain will subside in about ten days. The good news is, this means you're pregnant! Given all the extra water, I wouldn't be surprised if you're carrying twins. Through the miracle of the impenetrable womb your babies are safe," she said, her tone reassuring. "You'll be happy to know that you'll lose that belly that looks like you're seven months pregnant in a couple of days. Don't worry, you'll gain that back and then some in the next seven months."

I trusted Cindy; she'd been so effective and compassionate with her counsel during our infertility trials. The water did get reabsorbed, and I was released from the hospital within a week. But the bizarre pain, though less intense, persisted for the next three months, until the placenta was fully functional.

Cindy was right on another count too: I was pregnant with twins. When we later learned through ultrasound that we had a boy and a girl, I felt like I'd won the lottery. Acquaintances, learning that I was carrying twins, would invariably ask, "Boys or girls?" I beamed every time I got to answer, "One of each."

The second trimester of the pregnancy was relatively uneventful. Then came a routine checkup at week twenty-eight with my nurse midwife, Liza.

"You are 80 percent effaced, which means your uterus 'thinks' that these babies are about to be born. Right now," Liza said, pointing to an ultrasound picture of my son's head moving precariously down and out, "gravity is your enemy. Your goal is to keep these babies on the inside until week thirty-five."

"Seven more weeks?"

"That's right. Get some good books and DVDs. From now on you're officially on bed rest my dear; nurse's orders."

A friend from college summed up my feelings about this prescription: "Don't they know lying still is the definition of torture for you?"

Yup. Universal frying pan Number Three.

New Year's Eve 2002 was vivid, with the moon full and the snow glistening. Our dear friends Mishy and Chris, who would be the twins' godparents, had come bearing Mishy's mouth-watering rosemary roast chicken, some bubbly apple juice (no champagne for the pregnant momma), and their favorite pastime for the bed-bored—Rummy Cube. Midway through the game, I felt a rush of warmth and wet between my legs. My midwife confirmed our suspicion over the telephone. "Your waters have broken, Sara. You need to get straight to the hospital."

Twenty minutes later, we arrived at our small local hospital, where I was given a shot of steroids (to mature the babies' lungs) and antibiotics (to prevent infection).

"You guys are off to Baystate," the nurse midwife said. Baystate is our closest big-city hospital. "Your twins are too preemie for us to handle safely here." As the clock struck midnight, Joe and I welcomed 2002 with a fleeting kiss before I was whisked into an ambulance and sent speeding to Springfield, an hour away. Mishy, Chris, and Joe kept pace in their cars right behind us.

Conventional wisdom states that babies must be born within twenty-four hours of their waters breaking, so I thought we might get New Year's twins. But at the hospital we learned about other options. Since I was at thirty-three weeks, the next two weeks of gestation were critical to the babies' safe development. The doctors said every day the twins could stay "on the inside" was a gift. They would monitor me for infection. If none developed, we could wait ten more days.

For the next week-and-a-half I was strapped and monitored, injected and measured, cuffed and fed. Joe brought me mocha frappes to fatten up our little girl, who, according to ultrasound calculations, was weighing in at about three pounds. He played endless games of rummy with me and slept by my side on the uncomfortable hospital cot.

We'd entered the world of high-tech medicine, far from my dreams of a natural birth. We'd been warned by our midwives that the chance of avoiding a Cesarean on our high-risk obstetrics floor was close to zero. Terri, who worked with Liza as a midwife, explained that "[midwives] are trained to catch, and doctors are trained to cut." For fear of malpractice suits, for their convenience, the babies' safety, or for whatever other reason, these doctors seemed to prefer the predictability of an operation over the mystery of labor.

The delivery would take place in the operating room in case of an emergency, and hospital policy prohibited anyone but the spouse from being present in the OR. But I was unwilling to give up my vision of having three people at the birth: Joe for me and a trusted woman friend for each baby. We finally got the head of obstetrics to sign an agreement that unless an emergency C-section was needed, Joe and two others could be with me. I would labor in my hospital room, where others could be present.

The day of an amnio and labor induction, both of which I dreaded, arrived. That morning I began to feel contractions. Fetal monitors strapped around my waist were feeding data to the nurses at the center of the floor. Our favorite nurse, Tracy, came flying into the room, beaming. "Whoohooo," she cried, "you're in labor!"

Labor had begun spontaneously, a miracle in itself. I had contractions every couple of minutes, lasting a full minute. Birthing classes and books proclaim that during early labor the mother experiences contractions lasting thirty seconds, followed by significant periods of rest. Forget it. Steady intense pain was followed by more intense pain, which was followed by excruciatingly intense pain.

My birthing team arrived. Alisa came, carrying a bouquet of bird-of-paradise. Then Kristen, a certified nurse midwife, who had done her OB nursing training on the same hospital floor and knew the senior physicians and nurses there. Then Lynnie, queen of compassion, who had attended seventy-five births as a doula (a birthing coach). These three women and Joe labored with me for nine hours until the head of OB, Dr. Lucy Bayer (pronounced "bear"), arrived to examine me. Her stature true to her name, Bayer towered over the young male resident who shadowed her. She had the aura of a woman with no time to waste. She did a manual pelvic exam and found I was only two centimeters open after sixteen hours of labor.

"You need to prepare yourself that this birth is not going to go the way you wanted. I know you are someone who likes to get things done, but this is not something you can will to go your way," Bayer said. She looked down at me strapped to the table. "You're forty-one; you've been on bed rest for seven weeks; you have twins. Twins distend the uterus so that it doesn't contract effectively. Your babies are at risk. I know you want a natural birth, but death is also natural at birth. This is my one-thousandth labor and your first. Everything in my experience tells me you're going for surgery; it's time to accept that and get ready. You've got two hours."

As she left the room, images of the *Wizard of Oz*'s Wicked Witch turning the hourglass over on Dorothy flooded my mind. I could barely stay inside my skin. I felt like a caged animal, in agony, trapped on the hospital bed, hooked to two fetal monitors, an IV, and with a head monitor through my vagina resting on my son's scalp.

Tethered to a three-foot radius. I had screamed with every contraction to give sound to the pain. But when Bayer left the room, I let go a wail that came from a different place, a place of longing, heartbreak, and grief. I sobbed, shook, and puked. There had been so much surrender in this pregnancy. I had joked about going for my PhD in Surrender Studies and resigning as CEO of Control Freaks Anonymous. Was it time now, in the finale of this opening act, to surrender the dream of a healthy birth without surgical intervention? I remembered talking with Terri and her concept of the DNA of the Soul: two strands of will and surrender woven in delicate balance. What was called for now?

Time to pray for a miracle.

"Let's get you off this table," Joe said. "You've got to get vertical and get gravity going for you. You can do this, Sara." I focused my intention with a concentration I'd never experienced, digging into the essence of my being to find the place of opening, leaning physically and spiritually on Joe and the women surrounding me. They encircled me, speaking words of encouragement. "You can do this, Sara; you will do this. Those babies are coming naturally. Screw Dr. Bayer."

Bayer returned ninety minutes later, practically scrubbed and with scalpel in hand. She checked my cervix one last time. "Unbelievable," she said. "I never would have predicted this. You're ready to push these babies out! We're back on track." She left the room as briskly as she'd entered.

We cheered.

An hour later our son, Samuel Aaron, was born, followed eight minutes later by our daughter, Maya Freda. They were immediately whisked away to the Neonatal Intensive Care Unit. The first time I would hold them skin-to-skin against my chest would be twenty-four hours later, while they were hooked to monitors and IVs. I cradled the three-and-a-half-pound, fourteen-inch Maya between my breasts while Joe held Sam. It was a moment of pure, ecstatic, heart-opening joy. A feeling transcendent and exquisite. My heart opened like an orchid when flesh-to-flesh with the miracle of this child.

Though both children were fundamentally healthy, Maya was less than four pounds and Sam had initial respiratory challenges from the eleven days he'd spent inside a pierced amniotic sack after my waters broke. (Maya, whose sack remained intact, was unaffected by this.) Both were small enough to need an incubator and extra care until they could do four essential things on their own: suck, swallow, stay warm, and gain weight.

The following week in the Neonatal Intensive Care Unit (NICU) is a tale for another book. Suffice to say, the natural post pregnancy hormonal plunge, combined with the onset of milk in my breasts and a mother's instinct to have newborn babies on her skin, coupled with the hospital's policy that parents must sleep outside the hospital drove me wild. Add the high-pitched ringing of bells and whistles alerting NICU nurses of babies' arrhythmic hearts and drops in their oxygen saturation or respiration rates and my emotions were like a Coney Island roller coaster. One minute I was ecstatic at the miracle of these babies and at every ounce they gained, the next minute devastated by my physical distance and the unknowable term of our NICU sentence.

When we were finally released to go home, with Maya now weighing in at the requisite four pounds, the moon was once again full. Twenty-eight days had passed since our New Year's Eve ambulance adventure. With a momma bear's instinct and persistence, I determined that I would nurse these babies to health and vitality, no matter what it took.

Breastfeeding is widely considered essential for at least the first year for babies' healthy weight gain, brain function, and the creation of antibodies for immunity. The twins' preemie status left them vulnerable from the start, and there was no question I would nurse. College sports, Outward Bound, and Israeli Army training all paled in comparison to the physical challenge that ensued.

My kids did not sleep for more than two hours straight. And via Murphy's law of babies, they of course, choreographed a syncopated sleep schedule. One up at one, three, and five; the other at two, four, and six. For the next eight months I did not sleep more than two hours at a stretch. When they finally began to sleep through the night, they were vital, thriving, and doing all the things that eight-month-olds should. And I was physically depleted, sucked dry.

With rearview mirror clarity, I now see that the hormonal flood of IVF, followed by a twin pregnancy, followed by NICU, and then months of sleep deprivation was a recipe for disaster for my bipolar brain. In retrospect it is a testimony to the power of the mothering instinct to nurture the most vulnerable to health that I didn't plunge into my next depression sooner.

I want to take a moment to shout out to new moms who are experiencing mood swings: please explore the potential that you, too, may be on the bipolar spectrum. My friend Annette Cycon, a clinical social worker for thirty years and a nationally acclaimed advocate and educator in perinatal mood disorders, says it best:

"When a pregnant or postpartum mom with extreme depression seeks treatment, her primary care doctor or a psychiatrist may give medications that unintentionally put her at serious risk. This is dangerous! Standard antidepressant medications like Prozac, Zoloft, and other SSRIs, when misprescribed, can send some women into mania, more severe depression, suicidal ideation, or worse. These moms feel completely hopeless and begin to believe that they will never regain a sense of joy or normalcy.

"In 2006, Drs. Cheryl Tatano-Beck and Jeanne Watson-Driscoll named bipolar II the 'depression imposter.' Powerful term. They warned providers and the public about the life-saving importance of differentiating between postpartum depression and bipolar II. Since that time, there has been much more research and education. Healthcare providers who understand the bipolar spectrum now have the tools to help women reel in their deepest, darkest depressions. Unfortunately, there are not enough providers with expertise in both perinatal mood and bipolarity. In addition, women feel there is tremendous stigma around receiving this diagnosis. Postpartum depression is bad enough—no new mom wants to have a diagnosis of bipolar disorder too! Yet, when they get the right diagnosis and are given the right meds, it's like flipping a switch for so many women! For the first time, they delight in their baby, and that brings tremendous joy. They feel grateful to be alive."

There were more challenges ahead for me as a mom. Though the kids mercifully began sleeping through the night, my full night's rest lasted for only a few weeks before Maya suffered severe and scary breathing challenges that were incorrectly diagnosed as asthma. The cruelty of two-hour sleep stretches returned as I was up around-the-clock with Maya, administering breathing treatments, and nursing her back to sleep. Though she loved her Daddy, she wanted and needed only me. Sucked dry to the point of utter exhaustion, I began the familiar descent into depression, more terrifying now because I had these two small beings to nurture and protect.

Maya's condition worsened, and we were desperate to find the right diagnosis and the best treatments. Faced with a myriad of tests, medicines, doctors' opinions, and a brain that was now overwhelmed by the simplest information, I could not comprehend what to do.

Six years later, we would learn that Maya never had Asthma but was born with a blood vessel wrapped around her trachea that threatened her ability to breath. At that point she had a miraculous, life-saving surgery at Boston's Children's hospital. But in the interim, there were months of sleepless nights, and years of terrifying trips to the ER, with our little girl gasping for breath. I was on high alert, anticipating Maya's next attack, and that constant vigilance exacerbated the tenuous state of my nervous system.

Joe leaned on me in this domain of the babies' health, and I knew I needed my brain to work to make the right decisions for Maya's care. Once again, I got in touch with Juanita. Juanita had tried, like me, to cure her own depressions with all manner of alternative therapies. She'd finally consented to take prescription meds.

"It was the best decision I've ever made, Sara. I wish I hadn't waited so long to do it. You do not have to suffer. You don't deserve to suffer. You do have a genetic proclivity to a brain chemistry imbalance. You need to get medicine. I'm going to find the name of a psychiatrist in your area, and I want you to call. I'll check back with you tomorrow."

And so, at age forty-three, more than two decades after my first massive depression, I consented to see a psychiatrist and surrender to prescription medication. My circle of close friends persuaded me to do it. My friend Diane, went so far as to say, "I'm taking you to the appointment," because Joe was out of town on business. It was a blessing. I'd led my Israeli Army platoon in night navigation in the desert, but I could no longer read a simple road map.

Dr. Kathy Fisher [not her real name] determined that I was clinically depressed and prescribed Lexapro, one of the selective serotonin reuptake inhibitors and a cousin of Prozac. Three months later, I began to feel glimmers of hope. I could comprehend what

Maya's doctors were recommending and give her the suggested treatments. I began to trust the tools and medicines we'd been trained in to keep her out of the Emergency Room.

I slept, swam, and hiked, and Joe and I started making love again. I felt energy returning to my body and resumed my morning practice of getting up at sunrise to stretch and pray. The kids turned two, and for the first time since their conception I began to truly enjoy mothering and my beautiful children. What a relief.

On Lexapro, I felt increasing energy and vitality. Joe said it was as if I was "turbo-charged." I was outdoing myself. I got up at dawn, took care of the kids, wrote and published essays on mothering and sustainability, got in shape, started a new business partnership with four friends, and renewed my work with Joe as a corporate sustainability consultant.

My brother Bill called, concerned about my pace. "Sara, you're speeding. I'm afraid you're going to implode."

"I'm fine, Bill," I replied, annoyed at his mothering. "Really, don't worry. I feel great."

I attributed my abundant high energy to my disciplined diet, yoga and exercise, as well as gratitude for having escaped depression. When friends complained that I was talking faster and interrupting more than before I started taking Lexapro, I dismissed them as overly sensitive and politically correct.

"You know I love you," Alisa said. "I've been your number one cheerleader for fifteen years. I hope you'll hear what I'm about to say in that context. I'm worried about you, Sara. You're speedy. You've got a million ideas a minute and your fuse seems shorter than usual. Maybe you're on too much of the drugs."

Alisa was proorganics and antimeds, so while part of me registered her concern, another part dismissed it as New Age prejudice (as I'd once had) against Big Pharma. Later, I would learn that my family and friends had been right. My accelerating behaviors were classic bipolar II responses to Lexapro. Indeed, SSRIs are the antithesis of what I needed. For bipolar II brains they are essentially poison. They are now known to induce mania, create bigger mood swings, and increase incidence of suicide.

After a little over one year, Lexapro stopped working; it was making me worse. I sank into the worst depression I'd ever experienced, and developed new symptoms, including anxiety, tremors, night terrors, obsessive behaviors, and fantasies of suicide.

CHAPTER VIII

BRUTALITY OF
THE DAY-TO-DAY

It's a late winter day with snow still fresh from a blizzard. The sun has emerged brilliant, reflecting off the white expanse. None of this moves me. Leah and Larry, my hearty neighbors, have invited me to go cross-country skiing in the state forest across from our home. A year ago, I would have leapt at this invitation. Now I drag myself out of bed, struggling to remember where I've put skis, boots, and poles. What can I wear on an icy March day to stay warm?

Despite twenty-seven winters as a skier and ski instructor, I can't remember my layering system or where any of my ski clothes are. I barely have the physical energy to get to the car, let alone get out and propel my body against the will of gravity up any of the notoriously steep hills nearby. I don't revel as I usually do in the speed of the descent; I'm just glad to be down the hill not having broken or bloodied anything. I return home emotionally and physically spent. My body feels as if it lives on Jupiter, where gravity is much more intense; an hour's activity leaves me exhausted. No endorphins. All I want to do is sleep.

I've been an avid sportswoman my whole life. If it's winter, it's skiing, sledding, skating, snowshoeing; if summer, it's swimming, biking, blading, windsurfing. Joe likens me to the line from one of the Winnie the Pooh books: "Christopher Robin didn't care what it was doing outside, as long as he was out in it." I've always reveled in the feel of my body in nature and the gift of renewed spirit.

But now I feel geriatric—my muscles fatigued, bones aching, breath short. I also feel strangely disembodied, as if my brain doesn't compute messages from nerve endings and muscle sinews. I don't know why the typical "runners high" disappears. Perhaps endorphins are not manufactured, or are not released, or are somehow neutralized during the down-cycle of bipolar II. It's anybody's guess; the vast complexity of the brain is still uncharted. Whatever the cause, the result is that I get no relief or joy from physical exertion. I miss this greatly.

After skiing I feel too tired and heavy to sleep. I decide to do some yoga to try to calm down. I've been practicing yoga daily for eighteen years, but suddenly I cannot remember any moves or routines. It is as if my muscles have lost all their memory.

Simple everyday conceptual tasks I've taken for granted are nearly impossible. I'm submerged in depression. One day, it takes me three full hours to unpack groceries. I can't figure out where anything goes. I can't concentrate, can't remember what I'm in the middle of doing, from shelving the cereal boxes to putting away the tomatoes. In constant confusion, I'm unable to sequence actions or do simple addition and subtraction. I can't add more than a few numbers in a sequence. I forget my multiplication tables. Word recall is challenging.

This disease is humbling. I can't write a paragraph; it's nearly impossible to recall words like "humbling" or "calculus." This inability makes me miserable. I think of myself as a decent writer, yet I can't write.

Even though I graduated with an MBA from the University of Massachusetts, I can't recall the term for a particular economic concept. This drives me crazy for days. What is it? I can picture the concept but not the words for it. (Later when better, I remember it's the "law of economies of scale"—how the cost of manufacturing an item drops as you make more of them.) I hate not being able to find words for concepts I have used for years with ease.

Shopping malls and supermarkets are impossible; there are too many choices. The inability to make decisions leaves me overwhelmed with nervous anxiety and shame. How long can I stand in an aisle trying to choose between peanut butters? The large or the small? The organic or the inorganic? The cheap or the higher priced? The locally produced or the one that's less expensive, but from out of state? These decisions paralyze me.

Getting dressed in the morning poses a similar challenge. Deciding what to wear makes my heart pound and my breath hitch with anxiety. What goes with what? How do I choose colors? If it's cold enough to wear socks and there are none in my drawer, I'm at a loss. I stop doing laundry. It's too overwhelming to go through the sequencing it takes to fold, sort, and put away clothes. In the office and the bedroom and the kitchen, things pile up. It's too hard to remember where I put them; it's easier to have things in plain sight. But I hate this mess. The chaos makes me crazy, and I am embarrassed to invite anyone over into this scene.

I also can't do dishes. It's not that I don't want to do dishes, I really can't do them. I look at a pile in a sink, counters with crumbs and spilled ingredients, food that needs to be Tupperwared and put away, and I am overwhelmed. My brain doesn't know where to start, how to sequence the task, and how to keep going. I stare a lot. I'm incapable of getting my kids dressed and fed.

I fear the kids will get lost in the life-sucking vortex of our home. So we drive the forty miles roundtrip from our rural abode to spend the day with loving, tolerant friends in town. These trips away from the hearth drive my husband crazy. He needs unstructured time on our land to recharge and feels exhausted by my demands to keep moving. But home is a dark, oxygen-starved cave for me; I have to breathe to live.

I'm sure I'm not giving my kids the activities they need to thrive and compare myself ruthlessly to their friends' mothers, who provide gymnastics and piano and art classes. The thought of soccer overwhelms me. How do I find a team? Who do I call to sign them up? Where do I get uniforms and cleats and water bottles? And if I do buy these things, how do I keep the uniforms in a place I'll remember them for the next practice? I won't wash the socks and shirts because I'm afraid I won't be able to find them in time for the game. Then I'll be filled with shame that my kids look dirtier than the other kids. To get there, I'll have to buckle them in, bring snacks and water, gas up the car, and find the field in time for practice.

I know I can't do any of this, but I somehow try to do it anyway. The effort exhausts me. When we're back in our garage, I leave all the gear in the car, go inside, and collapse on the couch. Someone else will have to unbuckle the kids and make supper. I am done.

When a doctor or therapist or friend calls to offer support, I answer the phone from the couch. I scribble a note to attempt to remember what I've agreed to. But by the time I get to my calendar downstairs, I can't remember where I've put that piece of paper, and I have no idea what I've committed to doing. I used to keep my calendar on Microsoft Outlook, but my computer is down, and I don't have the energy or focus to fix it. I'm back to a paper calendar, which is never by the phone when I make an appointment. As a result, I miss commitments, I'm chronically late, or I forget a friend is coming over and I'm out shopping for food when they arrive.

I have always prided myself on reliability and punctuality and this sort of "flaky" behavior drives me crazy. I judge myself mercilessly for it, as I am sure others do. And who could blame them?

Money drains through us, adding more stress to our lives. Because I am so dependent, my husband can't work as much. He's doing everything he can to keep me alive, attend to the kids, and run our household. I'm nearly incapable of taking care of myself or my kids, so we hire childcare, cleaning help, and more. There's no way I can work at my high-powered, intellectually demanding job.

Moreover, I am frantically seeking solutions of all kinds, and these so-called remedies, supplements, and therapists are exorbitantly expensive.

Nothing works. I try every guru of every hoping-to-help friend: homeopaths, acupuncturists, chiropractors, Chinese medicine purveyors, and naturopathic doctors, each with their own theory of healing and corollary slew of supplements. Ring up a charge of

$350 or so for each of these visits. I spend thousands of dollars; our credit card debt soars.

When you have this disease, you are desperate for help and thus vulnerable to charlatans and would-be healers who don't have a clue about what they are dealing with. A man named Paul Sterling, I have changed his name, referred to me by a reputable colleague, claims to have the power to do distance healing. He calls me from three thousand miles away in Oregon. After a quick long-distance "scan" he finds that "walk-in demons have colonized" my body. He performs an exorcism over the phone for three hundred dollars.

Really? Nothing changes.

A chiropractor, recommended for his unique and effective alternative healing approaches, uses homemade tinctures that work on my "energy body." He determines which ones I need by placing crystals on my chakras. The cost? One-hundred-and-fifty-dollars for an hour. Then there's a dear friend's psychic healer who, for $250 an hour, tells me (in a finger-pointing tone) that DNA can be overcome, family history is irrelevant, and all I need is to get off sugar, meditate on my third eye, and open my crown chakra. Then I'll be cured. This is spoken with the arrogance and ignorance of someone who has zero experience with my disease.

As the days darken in the fall of 2006, I begin to panic. I've been sensitive to seasonal changes for years, always preferring the long, warm days of summer. If I feel this bad when it is warm and sunny, the dark and cold will kill me. Maya's mysterious breathing challenge is also much worse in the winter. The year before she'd suffered five dangerous pneumonias in as many months. Winter colds and flu are her trigger. I reason that if we take her someplace warm, perhaps her lungs will have the chance to strengthen and heal. Maya's situation, coupled with mine, convince us to head south to Florida, where my parents spend the winter. They offer to rent us a place in their neighborhood, delighted to be near the twins, their youngest, and presently most adorable, grandchildren.

But the Florida sunshine does nothing to ease my pain. Instead, I feel rootless and isolated from my support system of friends. My anxiety intensifies.

One morning, I'm in the kids' bathroom trying to find their toothbrushes and towels. Sam approaches, asking, "Momma, can you open this jar of peanut butter for me? I'm hungry." As he hands it to me, the jar drops onto the cold tile floor. It shatters, leaving the peanut butter laced with glass shards. It's a simple mistake any four year old could make. But I let out a bloodcurdling scream, and then scream again and again. Not because I'm mad at Sam. I know it isn't his fault, but the effort it will take me to secure another jar of peanut butter is too much to bear.

I'll have to find my wallet, my keys, get in the car, buckle both kids in, remember where the store is, get there, find a parking place, get the kids out of their car seats, walk with them through a sea of cars in a strip mall parking lot, remember what I need at the store, feel the dread of staring at endless shelves and choices of peanut butter, then do the whole thing in reverse to make it home. It will take more mental energy than I have on reserve.

Sam's tanned, innocent face turns pale as tears stream down his cheeks. He wails in fear. What is going on with his momma? I see the terror in his eyes and stop myself.

"Sammy, it's not your fault, you didn't do anything wrong. I'm sorry I'm yelling."

Confused but relieved, he lets me hold him. Meanwhile, my Inner Accuser is having his way in his righteous patronizing tone: "You are pathetic. You don't deserve to mother this beautiful, innocent child." I concur. My Inner Accuser is right.

Our friends Stan and Dalia are coming to Florida in January with their daughter, who is the same age as our kids. Joe's back in Massachusetts working. They invite me and the kids to go camping with them, on a pristine beach, one of the few left on the Florida coast where you can still camp by the sea in rustic cabins. Stan and Dalia are expansive hosts and gourmet cooks who live life in huge gulps and are unfailingly generous in sharing their abundance. Where I'd bring ramen noodles and trail mix on a camping trip, Stan roasts duck over an open fire, bakes potatoes snugged into the coals, then serves these with Margaritas and fresh lime, a linen napkin draped over his wrist.

But Stan and Dalia don't know about my illness, and they aren't people I feel comfortable sharing the details with. Dalia knew I'd been struggling with something, so I do tell her it would be tough for me to organize packing for a camping trip, especially with Joe away.

"Don't worry," she tells me over the phone. "We'll do it all. We've already got the cabin reserved; we've got coolers and ice chests and tons of food. You know Stan loves to cook; he won't let you help anyway. I'll bring sleeping bags for the kids. Just bring your toothbrushes and we'll be fine."

"OK," I say, knowing that this adventure with two healthy, boisterous adults will be excruciating for me. But the kids will love camping with their friend, and I want to do this for them.

Because of his *joie de vivre* and sunny nature I imagine Stan has never known anything close to what is going on in my head. He phones me the morning we are leaving with a simple request: "We've got everything, but I forgot a bottle opener. Could you pick one up and a six-pack of beer on your way here?"

I feel my throat clench and panic come over me. I can't explain to Stan why this simple request is putting me over the edge; that if I have to stop for a bottle opener and beer, I don't think we can come. Packing overnight gear and clothes for two kids, navigating to a new place on my own, and keeping the kids from meltdowns on the way is already daunting. I don't want to sound selfish, but I have no choice but to tell a small part of the truth.

"I'm not sure I can. I'll have the kids in the car seats and I don't want to stop."

Flooded with shame and embarrassment, I know Stan must think I'm bizarre, uptight, ungrateful. They are doing everything, and I can't pick up a six-pack of beer?

"I'll ask Mary to get it," Stan says. "She's coming today too."

I survive the weekend thanks to Stan and Dahlia's generosity. But the entire time, instead of enjoying myself, I am anxious to leave. Keeping a façade of levity sucks me dry. Driving the three hours south on Florida's highway 41 I am bone-exhausted, dehydrated, and shaking. Thankfully, Joe is home on our arrival. I pass off the kids to him, drag myself to my room, close the curtains, and slam the door. I'm exhausted by human contact, yet too scared to be alone.

In February, one of my closest friends, Lisa, comes to Florida to visit with her daughter Susan, who has been best friends with Sam and Maya since they were *in utero*. Lisa knows I'm in crisis.

Not long after she arrives, I tell her about my dilemma of the moment: I have a new set of prescriptions from a psychiatrist who practices "integrative psycho-pharmacology." That is, he's prescribed allopathic meds as well as all kinds of herbal, nutritional, and homeopathic supplements. But I've had to travel fifteen feet from the room where I've been speaking with him and taken some cryptic notes, to the kitchen, where I keep the numerous supplements he's recommended. During those fifteen feet, I've lost focus. By the time I reach the refrigerator to locate the supplements, I've forgotten what he's recommended. And I can't follow my own notes on what to do.

Lisa recommends that I make a chart to track times, dates, and dosages of the various meds. This proves overwhelming. I can't order my thoughts enough to focus on the task. But since my friend has come all this way and is here to support me, I want to try for her. I struggle to remember what I'm doing, yet I draw a blank. My expression must reflect this, as I see the sad, compassionate wince on the face of my friend who knows me to be, in her words, "brilliant."

"Wow, Sara," she says, catching her breath. "I didn't realize it was this bad."

"It is."

Stripped bare, vulnerable, in the depths of my dysfunction, I feel embarrassed and relieved to be seen in the raw, in my inability to process simple information. Maybe having seen the real me, Lisa can help figure out what to do.

That afternoon, Lisa comments on my bloody fingers. When my illness flares up, so does a corollary compulsion. I pick at the cuticles of my fingers until they bleed profusely. And no matter what I do, I can't stop. I cover them with Band-Aids and then pick the Band-Aids off. I put gloves on at night and resume the addiction in the morning.

My kids see me bleeding and say, "STOP, Mom, your fingers are all bloody!" I'm painfully aware of the example of self-mutilation that this models for them, and still, I can't stop. My fingers burn with pain. Clothes, sheets, and towels get bloody. Strangers look at my hands with conspicuous horror. My husband buys me white silk gloves. They get bloody, and I lose one. It's a horrible, embarrassing, excruciating compulsion, but I can't stop.

My friend Lara googles the behavior and finds this: "Excoriation disorder (also referred to as chronic skin-picking or dermatillomania) is a mental illness related to obsessive-compulsive disorder. It's directly linked to chemical imbalances in the brain," the site explains.

"It's not your fault," Lara tells me, and her kind words lift some of the shame. She prints out the results of her internet search. The text recommends a particular form of B vitamin. I try it in large doses. It doesn't help.

My fingers are outrageously painful, and I'm humiliated by my powerlessness over this compulsion. My fingers get infected. My life is unraveling, my brain isn't working. I can barely care for myself, let alone the twins. I don't think it can get any worse than this.

I am wrong.

CHAPTER IX

ICY PSYCHIATRISTS, BLOODLESS NEGLIGENCE

I've been referred to my first psychiatrist, Dr. Kathy Fisher (I have changed her name), by a friend and respected therapist. She has sent her own patients to Dr. Fisher. Still, I'm skeptical about psychiatrists.

Why the mistrust?

Perhaps it was a movie I'd seen long ago in which Jessica Lange played a gorgeous but slightly crazy leading lady. The psychiatric team forces a lobotomy, against her consent. Lange is wrestling and screaming. The injustice of this turned my stomach.

Or perhaps it was our neighborhood friend Mrs. Callihan, mother of six, who was an elegant and refined lady until she began taking drugs for her moods. The story we kids heard was that "the doctors" had misdiagnosed her and given her overdoses of the wrong chemicals. Her face and figure puffed out and she wore too much pink rouge. She also developed a constant tremor and chain-smoked. Scary.

Perhaps it was a leftover from my childhood perception of my mother's condition and treatment. Though my mother did well on lithium for decades, my harsh judgment was that her (male) doctors were infantilizing her. I didn't like it. I didn't like men telling women what to do, period. I didn't like that my mother had been a victim of my father's abusive temper all the years of my youth, and that I had never known her to fight back and defend herself. Or defend the rest of us.

I wanted her to stand up like a mother bear defending her cubs, roar louder than my father could, and get him to sit down and behave. I saw her as powerless in the face of his violent rages. So I didn't trust her when it came to men, whom she would have seen as powerful, like her psychiatrist with the Harvard Medical degrees. I imagined that she acquiesced and followed whatever his arrogant prescription might be without ever challenging his opinion.

I'm more comfortable seeing a woman than a man for a diagnosis and prescription. Reluctantly, I consent to the appointment with Dr. Fisher. My friend Diane drives me. "This is a breakthrough moment for you, Sara," she says beaming. "Healing time."

But after asking only a few simple questions, Dr. Fisher proclaims me depressed and gives me a prescription for Lexapro, an SSRI, despite my mother's positive history with lithium, an indication that she had bipolar. Why does Fisher assume I have unipolar depression?

Given that mental model, she starts me on Lexapro, which I later learn can be dangerous to bipolar patients, causing weight gain, sexual dysfunction, brain tremors, and a host of other equally delightful side effects. She says nothing about the trauma it can cause upon withdrawal.

Several months pass. I still feel lousy, hopeless, irritable, and lack energy. Then I slowly begin to feel better. My energy returns, along with my ability to focus, to exercise, nap, and laugh. I am a convert and think the drug a miracle. I tell others trudging through on St. John's Wort or other alternative treatments they don't deserve to suffer. Like them, I say, I'd resisted medication for many years, but in retrospect, that was a sad waste of life. There was a way up and they, too, should try drugs. I feel happy and grateful that these things work.

Until they stop working.

The descent accelerates, snowballs; it's a vicious cycle. The less I want to do, the less I can do; the more I feel shame, the less I want to be seen; the more isolated I feel, the less capable of making human connection; and on and on. I forget to shower, and what's the purpose, anyway? It's too much trouble to wash my hair, and when I'm in the shower I don't remember if I've washed it. It's too hard to shop and prepare food, so I eat whatever I can scrounge up, usually carbohydrates and sugar. These exacerbate the situation. I don't do laundry because it's too hard to fold and put away clothes. And I don't file or put anything away because I won't be able to find it. Entropy rules and I'm sickened by it. It's like the last time I was depressed: endless, relentless exhaustion and aimlessness. I have no motivation to get out of bed. I'm not inspired by anything, not even Joe or my children. I'm disgusted by the filth in my house, by my appearance, by the chaos that is taking over.

Now comes the "judge," making things worse still. The judge is a demon that must reside in this hell I've descended into. I'd never thought about demons or judges, never imagined these images in my healthy life. In fact, I have strong self-esteem. But here in hell, where the demon lives, he is relentless, cruel, vicious. He NEVER lets up on me, blaming me incessantly for the horror in my home, my body, my relationships, my work. His voice is insidious, manipulative, nasty. "You never really did anything meaningful in your life anyway. It's been a waste. You're ruining your kids. You're a terrible mother, a pitiful mother. Everything you touch turns to death. Look at the plants in this place, the filth. Maybe everybody here would be better off if you were dead. Have you thought about that?"

I do, daily. But I'm too scared of the abyss on the other side. And thankfully sane enough to know that my suicide would ruin the lives of my children, my parents, and my husband, and break the hearts of many others.

So here I stay, on this planet, but barely. I have daily imaginary conversations with a late friend, Marjorie, who had been full of life and had died recently after a dogged fight with cancer. She hadn't wanted to go so soon, leaving her dark-eyed young daughter and a sweet new marriage. "Marjorie," I plead, "is it better over there where you are?" She never answers.

Suffering, already on drugs, I turn to a new psychiatrist for help. An Irishman, Dr. Sean O'Reilly [name changed], whose office was closer to my home. Dr. O'Reilly's response is typical of psychiatrists who do not understand the critical distinction between unipolar depression and bipolar II depression. He suggests we increase the Lexapro. If it had worked before, why not try more?

I get sicker. Excruciating headaches. Nausea. Dangerous fatigue, such that I start to fall asleep on the highway even when driving the kids. Dr. O'Reilly says, "Let's add Wellbutrin." Wellbutrin is in a different class of drugs that sometimes works well with Lexapro. "Kind of gives you a lift," or something to that effect. "We'll start slow and see how you tolerate it."

One night, I start to feel my energy coming back. I stay up until 4:00 a.m. answering emails. A little buzzed, but this is better than depression. But then, I can't sleep at all. I tremor, toss and turn, buzzed. Feel like I've drunk way too much coffee. By daybreak I am exhausted. Driving to Dr. O'Reilly's office, I almost hit a tree. A cop pulls me over and charges me for speeding. After he tickets me, and leaves, I scream to unseen gods. This, too?

Dr. O'Reilly is friendly enough, but I have to remind him of my name and the specifics of my history every time I see him. This pisses me off. I've told this guy my gut-wrenching story, yet he can't distinguish me from the pack. Really?

Since I am getting worse on Dr. O'Reilly's drug regimen, I decide to return to Dr. Fisher. She'd helped me before, she was a woman, and she had a slightly better "bedside" manner. At least she remembers my name. Even though her office is an hour away, she no longer takes my insurance, and she charges $250 for the first return visit. Ouch!

Fisher spends no more than ten minutes with me. She says, "Get off the Wellbutrin and try Prozac. Sometimes another SSRI will work when one stops working." We begin at 20 mg, then 30 mg, then 40 mg, the top therapeutic dose. This through the summer, the time I usually revel in being alive in the outdoors. I can't enjoy the sun on my skin or the wind in my face. I just want to sleep . . . go away . . . leave the planet. I call her on a particularly bad, suicidal day. I almost beg her to look at my family history, which she continues to ignore.

"My mother's been successfully on lithium for three decades. Since lithium works, isn't she bipolar by definition? Isn't that genetic? Shouldn't I try what works for her?"

Dr. Fisher scribbles a scrip for a new med called Lamictal. I'm to take it in addition to Lexapro. "The problem with Lamictal," she says casually, "is that if you have an allergic reaction to it, you can die. So just keep on the lookout for a skin rash."

This was less than comforting: I could die from suicide or I could die from a poisonous drug.

"Just be patient, the drugs take time."

I don't know how much patience I have left.

She ushers me out of the office, our twenty-five-minute session over. "I'll see you next month." I hand my check to the receptionist, who barely looks up from behind her glass window as she mumbles something about Dr. Fisher's availability.

Despite her awareness of the risk of death from Lamictal, Dr. Fisher does not monitor my progress on it. I begin to take it, but I'm panicked by the risk. Receiving zero support from my psychiatrist doesn't help.

I continue to experience the excruciating pain of the day-to-day struggle and the feeling of being high on a cliff without belay (a rope strongly secured to an object) with no one in sight who knows how to save me from the abyss.

With no improvement, I decide to follow the advice of a trusted friend in Boston who was well connected with its movers and shakers. Perhaps her friends at Harvard Medical School can refer me to the preeminent doctors in Boston. I had to try something. After a six-week wait—eternity—I get an audience with Dr. James Weinstein [name changed], the psychiatrists' psychiatrist. His office was in my hometown of Brookline.

Maybe this would bring me luck. Weinstein didn't take my insurance and charged three hundred dollars an hour. Whatever. By now I was so in debt, who knew whether I'd ever recover financially. That worries me, but I'll try anything.

Dr. Weinstein spends a good sixty minutes with me, seems genuinely curious, and does a thorough interview. I'm hopeful. But in the end he says simply, "Stick with what Dr. Fisher is recommending."

"That's all?"

He continues reassuringly, "I'll stay on your case."

I never heard from him again.

That's when we head south for the winter. Dr. Fisher drops the Prozac and gives me prescriptions for Lexapro and Lamictal but she won't do consults by phone while I'm away. "I only see patients in my office," she says.

She sends me, suicidal, with two deadly drugs in my hands, off to Florida. No follow-up, no contact, no referrals, or communications with colleagues in Florida. Was she out of her mind? Irresponsible? Burned out? Cynical? What was she thinking, sending me off with suicidal ideation and a prescription for a drug that is deadly if not closely monitored.

Whatever the cause, today, in retrospect, in my right mind, her behavior was unconscionable. No, that word isn't strong enough. Like Auntie Em says to Almira Gulch, the would-be wicked witch in *The Wizard of Oz*: "Being a Christian woman,

I don't have the right words for YOU." OK, I'm not Christian, but you get the point.

There was no science to this science at all. In the case of these three reputable psychiatrists, there were no blood tests, no controlled experiments, no tracking of genetics. Just hit-or-miss. A bit of this, a tad of that. Trial and error. With their patients' lives, families, and worlds at risk.

Nothing had worked, the professionals seemed clueless, and I felt sicker—more anxious, more mercurial in my moods, more reactive, with more suicidal ideation—on the drugs they'd prescribed. I decided to take myself off them in Florida. I had met a sweet New Age woman who'd done the same for herself with success. She had handed me a book by a well-respected pharmacist, Armon B. Neel Jr.: *Are Your Prescriptions Killing You?*

I might be better off without the drugs. I believed in that possibility. Thus began my withdrawal from Lexapro and Lamictal. It was dizzying. One blogger described withdrawal from Lexapro as follows: "I've gone off heroin and off Lexapro and I'll take the heroin any time." His description of his experience validated my own: crazy dreams, irritable moods, brain shivers. Yes, feeling like your brain is shuddering in its skull. It's not pretty.

In a 2007 *New York Times Magazine* piece, "Dr. Drug Rep," psychiatrist Daniel Carlat described his experience of being recruited by Wyeth Pharmaceuticals to represent their latest antidepressant, Effexor. Strikingly honest in his portrayal of his slow but steady decline into becoming a salesman for the drug, Carlat explained how he was enticed to do the job: a weekend at the Waldorf for him and his wife, tickets to a Broadway show, and

$750 an hour for calling on his psychiatric colleagues to convince them that Effexor was the drug of choice.

About a year into this, to his credit, Carlat realised he had become nothing more than a drug pusher. Only in his case, selling drugs was legal. He used his stature as a credible physician to influence his peers. And for financial reward, he forfeited his scientific judgment.

According to a psychiatrist, to come off Effexor, the withdrawal symptoms feel like your brain is quaking in your skull. There are a slew of other nasty potential side effects from this drug that plays Russian roulette with your brain chemistry, including dizziness, drowsiness, anxiety, nervousness, insomnia, vision changes, nausea, vomiting, diarrhea, changes in weight or appetite, dry mouth, yawning, and increased sweating.

Imagine: You are vulnerable, hopeless, imagining suicide as pain relief, and a professional you've entrusted your life with prescribes a drug he's being paid to sell you.

At best, being paid to prescribe certain drugs is unethical. Salespeople like this should do prison time—just like their counterparts who sell illegal drugs. No, they should do more time because they are abusing their power, and they know it. It is a classic conflict of interest, with potentially lethal results.

Did any of the first three psychiatrists I saw have financial ties to drug companies? I don't know. But after reading Carlat's article, I wondered. I was prescribed Lexapro, Wellbutrin, Prozac, and, for a brief period, Effexor, which also made my brain feel like it was banging up against my skull.

Only the second of these doctors' services was covered by my insurance company, but I had terrible results with Dr. Weinstein and sought further help. The next three charged $250, $300, and $300 per hour, irrespective of whether their treatment had any positive effect. I'd drive an hour to Dr. Fisher, she'd look at me, scribble out a new scrip and send me on my way for $85 (her fifteen-minute rate). No follow-up, no inquiry about why I'd missed an appointment, never a suggestion that I seek other kinds of therapeutic support. Just a scrip, a fee, and "See ya."

Here's a law I'd advocate for: Psychiatrists who prescribe drugs should be required to work in tandem with a social worker/psychologist or other professional counselor. The medicines are too powerful, the depressed patient is too vulnerable, and the risk of death is too high to entrust these people to psychiatrists alone, many of whom have the norm of spending twenty minutes with a patient and then prescribing medications that can be lethal. Steady follow up in partnership with a therapist is essential.

CHAPTER X

BIPOLAR II

At the end of March, we drive back to Massachusetts from Florida. It's still icy, raw, and gray, but I find solace being back with my circle of friends. Lisa has told our friends and family I'm in truly bad shape. She decides to create a triage team to pull me out of the pit I'm in. She emails my closest friends, saying I need someone to find me a psychiatrist, a therapist, and a body worker; someone else to cook and put food in the freezer so we can feed the kids; someone to give Joe a break and help with childcare; and lots of people to get me out of the house and walking.

It's my sister, Martha, who finally finds a responsible, caring, skilled, dedicated psychiatrist, Dr. Michael Perlman. Given our mother's history, Martha agrees with me in suspecting that I am bipolar, so she researches doctors with expertise in affective disorders. She gets the referral from a Pilates client in Boston who is a therapist. Joe makes the appointment for me on a Thursday afternoon. But the idea of driving thirty-five minutes, finding Dr. Perlman's office, and getting there on time is too daunting. At our next gathering, I tell my women's circle I have this appointment, but I'm afraid to go alone.

"I'll take you," Annette says in her characteristic upbeat tone.

We arrive at Dr. Perlman's office at 4:00 p.m. for a thirty-minute appointment. I'm turned off by his office. Stacks of books and piles of papers litter the floor. There's barely a place for Annette and me to sit. How can this guy think straight in a mess like this?

Dr. Perlman sits down opposite us with his computer screen and Blackberry lit up. He's distracted, I think. He's not going to be able to focus.

At six foot four, Dr. Perlman has silver hair, a trim beard, clear blue eyes, and glasses. I like the silver hair. Maybe he has some experience.

My judgment about the disarray of his office melts away when he begins his intake with a series of pointed, clear questions no one else has asked me.

"When you were on Lexapro," Dr. Perlman says, "did it make you speedy? In other words, did you feel like you had five thoughts at once and had to express them immediately?"

"Yes."

"Did people give you feedback that you were interrupting them or were more irritable than usual?"

"Yes. My closest friend, my brother, and my husband all said these things."

"And you say your mother responded positively to lithium for three or more decades?"

"Yes, absolutely. When she came off it last year, she tanked. Then she had electric shock therapy. We all agree that ECT saved her life, but she's adamant against me doing it; she says she lost way too much memory."

"I'll put money on it: you're bipolar. No doubt."

Thirty minutes into an interview, and he's figured this out. How did the other four psychiatrists I've been to, including a published psycho-pharmacologist from Columbia University and the "best of the best" from Harvard, miss these simple clues?

Perlman is unequivocal in his diagnosis that I have bipolar II, or "soft bipolar." I later learn that he is informed by Dr. James Phelps life-saving book, *Why Am I Still Depressed*. Dr. Phelps is one of the leading researchers and clinicians on the bipolar spectrum.* My form of bipolar disease doesn't manifest in mania; I've never had the characteristic wild highs of mania. But it does show up in dark, persistent, debilitating depression. And because it shares the symptoms of typical depression, low mood, weight change, loss of memory, no joy in life, it is most often diagnosed incorrectly as unipolar depression. The patient is then prescribed one of the SSRIs—Prozac, Lexapro, Paxil—and sent on her way. Now I've learned about the disastrous consequences of this mistake.

SSRIs are toxic to the bipolar II brain. Everything I've been prescribed, everything I've taken until now, has made me much, much worse. Lexapro had nearly been a death sentence for me,

---

* I am honored to include an interview with Dr. Phelps, a brilliant resource on the bipolar spectrum in the second half of this book. His website, psycheducation.org, also found in this section is a deeply researched, accessible, practical, and powerful resource for anyone wrestling with bipolar.

inducing racing thoughts, sleepless nights, bloody fingers, and suicidal dreams.

I leave Dr. Perlman's office with a prescription for Lamictal and pay him the ten dollar copay required by my insurance company. Ten dollars. That's it. Dr. Perlman calmly and clearly explains to be effective and safe with the Lamictal, we'll "titrate" up very slowly and monitor for rash. We will not combine it with other SSRIs like Lexapro (as Fisher had done in the past). We will check blood levels as we go to confirm safety and efficacy.

He is reassuring, but at this point, I am still very wary of psychiatrists. I know I need a therapist who can act as a case manager to guide me through the maze of confusion, treatments, and advice I've received about how to get better. My closest circle of friends, several of them social workers themselves, have suggestions for who I should see.

One suggestion is Jennifer Brown, a woman I know from a Jewish spirituality study group we were in for a year, together with two fabulous teachers. I recall being moved by Jennifer's ability to articulate her understanding of and relationship to the Divine. Every time she spoke, I was struck by her wisdom and depth. Over lunch during the year of our study, she had confided in me that she'd had her own struggles with depression and that this history contributed to her decision to get a doctorate in psychology.

Now I'm in critical need of a therapist I can trust. I also sense that Jennifer loves me and my kids—our families had shared some holiday time together—and I hope that this personal connection might make her genuinely dedicated to my healing, unlike other psychologists who had been happy to take my one hundred dollars for an hour's session and forget my name by the next time we met.

The day after Annette drove me to Dr. Perlman and I'd received my new diagnosis, I saw Jennifer for therapy. Her office was sparse and windowless, but warm, with a well-worn beige couch for me to sink into. Jennifer asks me what's going on, so I launch into the tired story of my twenty-five years of depressions. I've told the same boring tale in so many offices that I have little affect in recounting it.

"How was your meeting with Dr. Perlman yesterday?"

"Perlman says I'm bipolar II. He's putting me on Lamictal. I don't know if he's right or if I'm on the right drug. He's my fifth psychiatrist in two years, and I don't trust any of them. The drugs don't work. I don't know if I'm still depressed because of the biochemical storm in my brain, or if I'm also the victim of the medicines I've taken over the past two years from lousy diagnoses and prescriptions."

Jennifer's demeanor is calm, grounded, present, compassionate. She is listening deeply and responding with genuine concern. I describe Dr. Perlman's logic, his attention to my family history, and my own patterns with depression.

She responds, "I think Dr. Perlman's reasoning is sound. I believe therapy is key to healing. I also know that for the bipolar brain, medicine is essential to regaining your biochemical balance. I'll work with Dr. Perlman. I'll contact him tonight and make sure we're in close touch, working together on your case. You aren't alone in this, Sara."

Later that evening, Jennifer calls. She says she's talked to Dr. Perlman. They've agreed to work together to determine if I am on the right track with this diagnosis and medication. "He's very open to working with you. He understands that therapy is an essential complement to the medicine. That in itself is refreshing. You're in good hands, Sara."

I exhale, feeling a speck of hope for the first time in a long time. Do I finally have a team that will stay on my case? Sick as I am, I'm still skeptical. Dr. Perlman had disclosed that he was a representative for GlaxoSmithKline, Lamictal's manufacturer.

He'd told me, "I do it because in thirty-five years of practice I see that this medicine really works. Light years ahead of the others. But I want you to know I do receive money from the drug-maker."

Well, there was a refreshing dose of honesty. Still, he has this hammer, and maybe he sees the whole world as a nail. How can his judgment not be clouded by his relationship with Big Pharma?

I hold onto this skepticism, along with a good deal of resentment, for the three-and-a-half months it takes for the drug to begin to work. The trick with Lamictal is that you must increase the dose at an excruciatingly slow pace. It takes me six weeks to reach the most basic "therapeutic" dose of 100 mg. At 100 mg I am as sick as ever.

I am scared to make phone calls. Will I remember why I dialed the phone? What will I say when I get on the line? Will I even be able to speak in coherent sentences? I call Dr. Perlman at his prescribed "office hours" at 9:00 p.m. He is available at this hour every night and always returns my calls within five minutes. Now that was different from other psychiatrists.

"You told me 100 mg was therapeutic," I accuse him. "Your miracle drug hasn't touched my disease."

Dr. Perlman was unflappable in the face of my attack. "Stay the course, Sara. We have the right diagnosis. Just stay the course." His voice is confident, and his concern and compassion reach me.

I exhale, drop my shoulders, soften. "What do you mean?"

"The efficacy of the medicine is not a function of how much you take, but of how much remains in your bloodstream. Different people's livers metabolize these things at different rates. You may have to get up to 200 or 300 mg before the drug has the same impact for you as it would for someone else at 100."

At an increase of 25 mg a week, this means I am looking at another four to eight weeks before we'll find out if Dr. Perlman's hypothesis is correct. I wasn't sure I could make it that long. But the alternatives—electric shock, the psych ward, back to Lexapro, or any of the twenty other antidepressants on the market, suicide—all of them looked even bleaker. I had no desire to live left, but somehow, a speck of maternal instinct remained. I would rather stay in purgatory forever than leave my kids with the legacy of a mother who had committed suicide.

"Stay the course," he repeats. "You can call me every night if you need to. But I know we're on the right track. You will get better." I'm not sure. I don't share his confidence. I still can barely get out of bed. But I am beginning to trust that this man knows something true about me. More than anyone to date. That knowledge, coupled with his skill and caring, gives me a glimmer of hope.

Dr. Perlman's explanation about blood levels versus dosage makes sense. But why have none of the other psychiatrists explained this? He prescribes blood level testing—something no one else had advised or required. I need to write this again in case you're reading quickly: No doctor in the two-plus years I'd been on antidepressants had ever prescribed a blood test.

I mention this to Dr. Perlman the next night when I call during office hours. "Are you sure I need a blood test? No one's ever told me to get one before."

"Sara, it's the only way we'll know for sure if you're at therapeutic dose," he replies calmly. "It's like an on/off switch. If you're below therapeutic levels, it's off; when you're at the proper dose it's on."

This makes sense. I ask Joe to drive me the next day to the closest hospital, twenty minutes from home, farther than I feel comfortable driving on my own. I don't mind needles; I watch incredulously as my blood is drawn. How can this red liquid, life-giver that it is, have betrayed me with dangerously screwed-up blood chemistry? The results take a week to process.

Dr. Perlman calls, pleased. After ten weeks of titrating up at 25 mg per week, I had just begun taking 250 mg of the drug and my blood levels were at 4.9, well within the ideal 4 to 6 range that studies recommend.

"It will take two to three weeks at this dosage for you to really gain the benefits of the medicine. Stay the course."

I'd come this far; OK.

By Divine grace, or some team of researchers in a window-less laboratory at GlaxoSmithKline, or Dr. Perlman's mother, or Jennifer Brown's wise and loving counsel, or the boundless support of my husband and closest circle of friends, or all the above, I began to feel better. Slowly at first, but in clear and remarkable ways.

Yet I keep wondering about the other four psychiatrists I saw before meeting Dr. Perlman. What happened to them that they stopped learning? You have to believe that these people started out as idealistic medical students. They wanted to be doctors to help people, to heal suffering.

In the end, they caused it.

CHAPTER XI

JOE WAS A ROCK

How can a marriage survive when one partner loses her sanity, her sexuality, her capacity to mother, to work, to love and support her lover, to laugh, celebrate, or appreciate life? How can the spouse who is healthy survive the mysterious abduction of his beloved? She was here in body, mind, and soul, in lust for life, and now it's as if some sadistic walk-in has taken over.

How can the one left alone survive the grief, anger, loss, fear, and mourning? How can he have the physical stamina to take on all the care and feeding of the children, the home, and the suicidal partner while also shouldering the entire responsibility for earning a livelihood? How can this person survive without cracking up, splitting the scene, or becoming vengeful or cruel himself while he gets none of his needs for care and nurturance met? Seems impossible. Had the roles been reversed, I doubt I'd have survived it with self and family intact.

I am simply lucky that my man Joe was a rock—solid, steady, tireless.

In writing this sentence I'm aware of the privilege I possess. Not everyone with this disease has a reliable partner who can provide emotional, physical, and financial support. This makes the path exponentially more difficult. If you are in this position, it's all the more important to reach out for the support of friends. If you love someone with bipolar depression who does not live with a caring partner, it is all the more reason for you to get serious and organized about showing up with a posse of support.

With Joe, it was as if he was running a marathon with no end in sight. Or, to continue the Greek metaphors, like Sisyphus, he was pushing the rock uphill for eternity. There was no way to know when, how, or if my brain would recover, and I would return to be the woman he'd fallen in love with, married, built a home with enthusiastically, and agreed to have more children with at age fifty, when his oldest was already twenty-three.

When we met, Joe described me as the strongest woman he'd ever known. He chose me because, having had two previous marriages, he knew he wanted a woman with whom he could truly partner, a woman who, as he liked to say, could meet him in his power. He'd joke, "When I finally met the strongest woman I'd ever known, I did the only logical thing a man could do—marry her."

A leader in the men's movement in the 1980s and 1990s, Joe was fluent in the language of self-reflection and personal history. He said that first he'd married his submissive mother, then he'd married his abusive father, and now, in me, he was marrying his soulmate—a woman who came of age with the second wave of feminism in the 1970s. Thank you very much; I didn't need a man to take care of me. I liked my independence, and so did Joe.

For the first three years of our long-distance courtship and the next three years of living together and marriage, the empowered part of me was the only part of me Joe experienced. When we made the commitment for life, witnessed at our wedding by one-hundred-and-fifty or so friends and family, I truly believed that part of me would prevail. I was open with Joe about the dark days of my past, but always framed them as such: past.

When Joe and I first experienced the depressed version of me, we were both shocked. Me, because I was sure this was history. Joe, because the woman before him was the quintessential opposite of the one he'd described as the strongest he'd ever known. I was suddenly and totally incapacitated.

By then we were full-scale professional partners in the business that sustained us financially. Business consulting at high-powered companies like Nike and Shell was intellectually and emotionally demanding, and suddenly, I couldn't do it. All the skills I relied on were gone. I had a reputation as a smart, reliable, energetic visionary, but I was now none of these things. It was as if I'd been hit with a debilitating and unexpected disease like cancer, but this was worse. A cancer patient is sick, while a bipolar woman is not only sick, she's lost her fundamental personality. It becomes hard to find the person you fell in love with and married. Still, through compassionate eyes, Joe could see the hidden essence of me.

He covered for me. Though he'd joined my business and was not fully comfortable in the private sector, he stepped up. "I miss my partner. I miss my soulmate," he'd report in confidence to friends. But for our public persona, he never let on that I was down. He followed through on all our professional commitments, his and mine.

In April of 2006 at age forty-five with four-year-old twins, after being on the wrong antidepressants for more that two years (this was before Dr. Perlman), my descent began in earnest. For the next sixteen months, that is 11,520 hours, I was in a bottomless free fall. One endless hour at a time.

Joe never let me go. Invoking the image from the film *What Dreams May Come*, where Robin Williams travels to the bowels of hell to retrieve his wife after she's committed suicide, Joe told me, "Just like in the movie, I'm going to hell and back for you." He could still find me, even though I could not.

Believing him gave me some measure of comfort. I would not suffer and die alone. (It's poignant to reread this story after Williams's tragic suicide in 2014 due to progressive dementia and mental illness. His sweet picture smiles at me from Wikipedia, where I'd looked up his date of death. I so wish he'd found the support he'd needed before he took his life.)

Remember, I could barely get out of bed. I was afraid to be alone with Sam and Maya, not because I would hurt them, but because I couldn't give them the basic care—food, water, clothing, safety—that they needed at age four.

I was more than dead weight; I was dragging the ship down. The things that emerged from my mouth were consistently negative. That is one of the insidious things about the disease; it somehow channels negativity. I remember being on the receiving end of this with my mother and it drove me, the visionary, to fury.

"Mom, just try to say something positive once!" I'd give her rudimentary coaching in turning her statements around. "Don't say, 'I'll never be able to climb that hill,' say, 'I can climb the hill.' Don't say, 'Shopping is impossible.' Say, 'I think I'll go shopping for some food now.'" This never worked, which made me angrier. Why couldn't she see all the beauty and gifts and privilege in her world?

Now I'd hear my own endless litany of negatives and have no more control over my words than I had over my new obsession with picking my fingers until they were bloody. "We'll never be able to finish this book. It's got the wrong message anyway." "I don't think you can go to Costa Rica with Lauren; you'll get sick down there and what will I do then?" "The kids are in the wrong school." "This house is killing me. The isolation—if I only lived in town." "The kids will never get the stimulation they need out here. There aren't enough girls for Maya to play with and the school is underfunded." "Winter is endless here, how are we ever going to get up that icy driveway? And no one can get down." "I don't think I can handle a birthday party for Sam and Maya. How can I do invitations?"

And on and on. I remembered from growing up how that kind of attitude was contagious, how one person's bleak views could suck down a whole room. When I was young, my mother's depression-fueled litanies about the tragedy of life drove me crazy. After Jack Kennedy died, "it was all over for our country." Then RFK and Martin Luther King. Vietnam and that "despicable" Nixon. "We were such a good nation when I was a child," she'd lament, "but now this country is hopeless. I feel sorry for you kids and what you're growing up into. I thought I could make a difference, but there's no use. I'm too tired to shop and you know I can't cook. I'm sorry, so sorry."

Now I heard her relentless negativity echoed in my own views and voice. But I couldn't stop. And I hated myself for it.

Joe never blamed me or shamed me for any of this. He'd say, "You're sick, it's not your fault. We're going to find a cure." He'd tell me I could still do things and encourage me, without pushing me. He knew I'd loved my spiritual teacher, Shefa Gold, and that she was doing a leadership training, which he wanted me to attend. Although I had no idea how I could manage this, he arranged the details, took care of the kids, and figured out payment so I could go. The hope was that this would be a healing experience.

After I'd recovered, the teachings from this experience and the friendships I made there turned out to be a great blessing. But during my illness, it was just another opportunity for self-recrimination and shame: I'm no leader, what am I doing with these people?

I think I was only able to receive this support from Joe because he was so clear that my illness was not my fault. He was so matter-of-fact in his solid, kind, Midwestern way that I took it as a given. From Joe's perspective it was: "This is just what you do for family."

When Joe's friend John got married and Joe couldn't make the wedding, he wrote John a poem about marriage. It read: "Sometimes marriage is like a flowing river, and sometimes it's like dragging your boat upstream against a rocky bottom. You do it one step at a time, day after day, until the current shifts and you find your way downstream again."

When I first read this poem several years into our marriage, I had no experience of what Joe was talking about. I thought he was being unnecessarily bleak. Our relationship was pretty blissed out at that time; we were going with the downstream flow.

I guessed Joe was referring to his previous marriages, with all their scrapes and bruises. Neither of us could know then that Joe was foreshadowing what would be his own experience for days, weeks, months, and years in his marriage with me. He would put his feet in the cold water and drag that boat up the rocky shore, scraping the hull, falling in the rapids, nearly hypothermic, but he would never, ever quit. He'd simply do it faithfully, day after day, never knowing if or when the current would shift, but never giving himself any other option than to stick with the effort. Because in marrying me, that is what he'd committed to, before family and community and beyond. And no matter what would ensue, he would live or die by that commitment.

Bless the rock of that man's soul; I never would have made it without him.

CHAPTER XII

MY SIBLINGS SHOW UP

It's spring 2008. Michelle Obama is my inspiration for chic, and I'm in her style of sleeveless, snug purple top and short black skirt with a slit above the left knee. Shoes match the skirt and toes match the top. Now strutting down Broadway in New York City on my way to a date with my publisher, Doubleday. A book I've coauthored has just come out. I'm here to meet with the editors and publicists. It's a heady thing to be at Doubleday, and I feel happy and proud seeing the handsome hardcover book representing fourteen years of work on the bookshelves. The meeting is upbeat, and I leave with ideas buzzing about how to get the word out.

That afternoon, I hike uptown through Central Park, feeling the pulse of the city, getting a sense of why people love this place. Central Park is lush in June. Azaleas and roses are in full bloom, and a rainbow of people are out enjoying an eighty-five-degree day.

Kids play tag, there's a coed softball team, a guy on the trumpet, an impromptu a capella chorus, and thinly clad lovers on the lawn soaking up rays.

I'm heading to a vegetarian restaurant on the Upper West Side and don't know exactly where I am. But I have a map, and it is close to noon, which means the sun is in the south. Walking with my shadow in front of me and sun on my back means I'm headed north toward my destination. I find it with ease.

What a difference a year makes. I'm so aware that in June of last year, I was contemplating a choice between an outpatient psych ward or ECT. There is no way I would have gone anywhere near New York to meet with high-powered folks at Doubleday. I would have been afraid to walk through Central Park on my own, for fear of getting lost. And who knows what kind of characters I might run into? It would have taken me at least eight hours (no joke) to pack for an overnight trip, a task that now takes twenty-five minutes, and at that, I would have forgotten shoes or jewelry or underwear. My clothes would be dirty because I wouldn't have done the laundry. I was lucky if I got a pair of jeans and a T-shirt together. My hair would be a mess because when I'd showered a few days back, I'd forgotten to wash it.

But this day, I revel in the freedom and diversity and dynamism of New York. I enjoy my walk to the East River for a sunrise stretch, joining an Asian man doing his morning tai chi, and the political conversation I have with Joel, my French-accented taxi driver from Haiti with a pro-Obama stance, even though it's New York, and he would have gone for their Senator Hillary Clinton if she'd won the nomination. I revel in the scent of pink blooming roses in Central Park, my ability to time events just right, and my sprint to Build-A-Bear and American Doll, because I'd promised Sam and Maya I'd pick up PJs and outfits for Bruno (the bear) and Goldie (the doll). "They need summer clothes, it's too hot now, Momma," Maya had said. And I still make it to my 5:00 p.m. Acela train home.

On the ride home I get a call from my brother Dan. Dan is a shark of a negotiator, with Mafia-like loyalty to the family. He'd been coaching me through a royalties dispute with my coauthors on the book. He takes great glee in the fact that we have a signed contract and thus the upper hand. He is laser-like in his analysis, taking his cue from *Star Trek*'s Mr. Spock. "Don't show any emotion," he'd said. "Take cool pills. Then state your case unequivocally. Do not waver. You have a signed contract—they have zero rights; we'll filet them with a knife."

I loved the use of the royal "we." Dan takes this personally. He's a massive offensive lineman on my team.

Dan is a dot.com guy who was a multimillionaire by the age of forty. Tall, dark, and exceedingly handsome, he was educated at a New England prep school, then Stanford and Harvard. This pedigree plus white privilege and his innate discipline, Vince Lombardi-esque love of winning, and steely calm demeanor make him a formidable opponent in any competition.

Dan is my elder by six years. When I was a child, he was G-d to me, even though he loved to shoot hockey pucks at me as practice. He'd give me a baseball glove and tennis racquet for defense, then fire away. "You'll thank me for making you an athlete," he'd say, wise sage at the age of twelve. "I'm making you tough." Years later, I do have a pretty good net game.

Dan's been CEO of several companies and is the kind of take-charge guy who is utterly confident in his ability to solve just about any kind of problem. His love and loyalty run long for family, especially for me, his kid sister. I think my illness devastated him because he could not figure out a way to fix it. He didn't understand, nor could he relate to the emotional pain of it. And given that we have such resonance on matters analytical and professional when I'm well, he couldn't fathom what had happened to me.

Still, he wanted to help and did so from his place of strength—finance. He didn't give us money when my debts were racking up from lack of work and excessive bills, his stance being that a financial bail-out was the job of parents, not siblings. But he did a detailed analysis of our financial status to help us climb out. Indeed, he created a two-year strategic plan showing us what real estate we had to sell, what loans we had to consolidate, and what expenses to cut so we could make ends meet. I couldn't follow through on any of this advice for lack of brain power, but Joe could, and it made a difference. Like my other sibs, Dan helped the best way he knew how.

My sister Martha is the oldest of four. She is extraordinarily empathic, compassionate, and caring. Martha is schooled in an impressive variety of alternative therapies and healing approaches; yoga, Pilates, meditation, astrology, homeopathy, body work. Where Dan will give you the bottom line in three sentences, Martha will offer compelling insights based on the complexity of a situation. Ten years my senior, she has always been my champion. When our mother was down with depression, Martha played surrogate. She is loving, optimistic, and curious about life. When

I was down with depression, she checked in on me daily, always offering a different modality or idea for healing. Listening and honoring my pain. Patient. There. And in the end, it was Martha who found Dr. Perlman. Who saved my life.

Bill is the oldest son and second-born in our family. He spent long hours trying to identify a cure. Characteristic of the men in my family, Bill likes to give advice. As things got worse for me, he became an advocate for electric shock therapy. Bill and I had been the key support for our mother when she went through ECT, and we'd acknowledged we'd witnessed a miracle.

"Honey" (as younger sister, that's what he calls me when I'm down), "if I couldn't work like you can't, I'd do it. Look at the marvel we witnessed with Mom. You could be back on your feet in three weeks."

My mother, on the other hand, was adamant in her opposition to this course. "You kids don't know how much memory I lost," she'd say to me in confidence. "It's a horrible side effect. There are years I don't remember. People I have zero recollection of that your father tells me we've socialized with. I will not let you do it."

As if she could still control the choices of her forty-something-year-old daughter. But her unequivocal stance on ECT scared me enough not to go down that path. What if I forgot my kids' friends' parents, or their pre-K teacher? How would I explain to them why I was gone for three weeks? In our small town, surely the word would get out. The stigma associated with ECT is even worse than that for manic depression. In retrospect, I'm grateful I listened to my mother on this count.

She passed in 2015, having suffered for decades with severe depression. She read an early draft of this book and gave me her blessing to publish it: "Spread the message, Sara." She had wanted to dedicate her brain to science. We failed to follow through on that, something I regret.

My father, who died in 2017 at 97, was a character who deserves a book of his own. He grew up as the son of penniless immigrants and worked his way out of Manhattan's Lower East Side on grit, perseverance, smarts, and good looks. A Jewish kid whose family experienced rampant anti-Semitism, he could pass as a perfectly Christian American thanks to his classic good looks. He's fond of relaying that he won the "Most Handsome" award in his New York City high school class of 750 kids.

He had achieved success by every standard American measure: wealth, a sixty-year marriage, ten grandchildren, a community that respects him. But he could never shake the shadow of the Jewish boy from the ghetto who never quite measured up to his blue-blood classmates at the Ivy League college he attended on scholarship. To the end of his long, successful life, he still felt beneath my mother's family with their New England accents, wit, and charm. He drove himself with a dogged determination to measure up to the standards of class, education, wealth, and charm he aspired to. He was tough on himself and tougher on all of us.

My father carried the visceral imprint of his mother, a turn-of-the-century immigrant from Poland who worked the night shift in a dress factory. After divorcing my dad's father and becoming a single mom in the 1920s, she scraped by day-to-day. His father, a mythological hero in our family, stowed away on a ship at fifteen with his seventeen-year-old brother to escape the Russian pogroms. The boys landed penniless and illiterate at Ellis Island, where their name was changed from Slimowitz to

Schley with the stroke of some bureaucrat's pen. These roots gave my father an empathy, compassion, and generosity for people in need that ran deep.

Still, as a man of the World War II generation, my father had no practice in naming or hearing emotions. His best form of support was to provide financial assistance. It was my dad who'd rented a house with a pool for us in Florida so Maya's lungs could heal.

These people, Martha, Bill, Dan, and my parents, Harriet and Len, formed my family of origin support network. That describes all of them, except for the King of Compassion, my yellow lab, Starhawk. This dog had a gift of unconditional love and acceptance that exceeded anything human I've known. Starhawk witnessed and supported me through the turbulence of my life changes: my marriage, building a house, starting a new business with Joe, surviving a near-death accident, infertility, a hellish pregnancy, the birth of the preemie twins, Maya's exhausting breathing treatments, and my depressions. There was virtually no one, not even my beautiful compassionate husband, whom I could allow to join me in that place of shame, hopelessness, and grief. But I could be with Starhawk. Lie on him. Bury my head in his neck. Cry. He would simply be. Present. Deep. Unconditionally loving. A place my weary heart could rest.

Despite all their own complications and challenges, my family gave me a web of support, like the net that catches the acrobat who's missed her trapeze. And when I was most at risk, they unequivocally showed up. Where would I have landed without them? Homeless on the streets of New York perhaps. But yesterday, I was cruising those streets, Michelle Obama chic.

CHAPTER XIII

TRIAGE

I'm lucky to have fiercely loyal friends. Joe says I'm the only person he knows who hasn't lost a friend since kindergarten. A friend who is an astrologer says it's in my chart. Somehow, I always seem to have prioritized my friends over my relatives, work, or hobbies. Seems I needed every one of them. It was triage time and my circles of friends—valiant, loving, compassionate, and practical—saved my life. As the depression took me deeper into the quicksand, they were my lifeline.

I'm part of a circle of seven women who have met the third Sunday of every month for twenty-four years. We've seen each other through birth and death, divorce and marriage, hospitalizations and healing, and all manner of personal failings and triumphs. Inevitably there's an email out from one of us going through a tough time, saying, "I don't know how I'd have made it without you all."

When my mood plummeted and my depression was incapacitating, these women showed up, big-time. Each in her own way, with her own gifts. Annette filled my freezer with homemade meals—ziti, lasagna, chicken—stuff kids eat. She also dragged me to Dr. Perlman when it was time. Diane, proprietor of "organize thyself," helped me find order in the household chaos. Jannie accompanied me to the hospital with Maya to see a pulmonary specialist, complete with Barbies, snacks, and books. Lynnie spent countless late-night hours on the phone with me, sharing her boundless well of compassion and insight. Morningstar took me on walks and sat with me, listening to music or reading poetry. And DJ held my hand and drove me to my first psychiatrist appointment.

There were also women apart from that circle, friends old and new from my rural town, a place where neighbors are short on pretension and long on acts of loving-kindness. Mara got me out weekly for long walks in the woods, listening with patience to whatever depressing tale I might offer. Patty brought food, gave me massages, told me she'd been there, too, and that I would come through this. Deva showed up numerous times, on a dime, when the kids or I were in crisis. When Maya needed to go to the ER, Deva was there on five minutes' notice to watch Sam. Lin walked the dog, offered prayers, listened without ever interrupting. Marilyn got me swimming (immersion was the most healing treatment I found), and when her eyes locked onto mine, she let me know that she, too, was a member of the "To Hell and Back Club." She'd been to the abyss with what she called "brain perseveration."

"I never thought I'd get better, Sara. But I did. You will too. I promise." Though I didn't believe that was possible, it was comforting just to be in the presence of someone who understood.

Then there were the women from out-of-town. Betsy, my college-roommate-turned-well-respected-clinical psychologist, who'd witnessed the start of all this, called me every Wednesday morning offering counseling strategies, opinions on drugs, and encouragement that I was doing everything I could to heal and should not feel shame.

Mishy, who researched names of doctors in Boston, made the two-hour drive out to our house to cook supper for my family. Nancy and Juanita, colleagues who lived on the opposite coast, offered to galvanize our entire professional network on my behalf. Andi, who called me every Tuesday morning, left roast chickens and noodle casseroles in the freezer, and made my kids laugh. Alisa did the internet research on my bloody fingers, brought me books and articles, offered to move in if we needed her.

Then there was Sara (by coincidence we share the same first name), who never let me go. Not a single day went by where she didn't call to check in, strategize, advocate, make phone calls and organize all the women mentioned above. Sara possessed a unique combination of constitutional optimism, boundless loyalty, problem-solving creativity, and a loving, compassionate heart. She simply refused to believe, no matter how many days, weeks, and months went by, no matter how many healing modalities we'd tried and failed, no matter how defeated I was, that I would not get better. And she was dog-on-bone adamant about this.

"You are NOT going to be the only person who does not recover from this disease. We are not letting you go down. We've got your back. We will not give up until we find a cure."

"But nothing is working. I'm so exhausted. I don't know how much longer I can take this."

"You are going to live, Sara. And you're going to look back on this time with relief, wiser and sweeter for what you've been through. You are going to thrive again. I know it."

You are blessed if you have someone in your life like Sara.

She did know it, and she was right.

When things were at their worst and my circle of friends and family were truly worried about my survival, Sara organized an e-list of many of the people I've mentioned. She organized the triage team, putting some of them on food, some on kid-care, some on medicine, some on finding a therapist, some on finding the right doctor. She put everyone in contact to support and encourage each other. I never read these emails, I didn't want to, but I knew they were happening and had a glimmer of hope that working together, these people could help.

And they did.

If you are suffering from any form of this disease, please don't do it alone. No matter how full of shame you feel, call in the supports. Humble yourself. Say "yes" to any and all offers of help. You need these people. And someday, you might have the privilege to support them in their time of need in return and feel blessed for the opportunity and ability to give back. As I do now.

If someone you love is suffering in crisis, don't wait for them to reach out to you. They cannot. Lean in to champion them. Rally their friends and family. They may need medical advocacy, they may need meals cooked, they may need rides for their kids, they may need you to take them to doctor's appointments, they may need dishes washed. Imagine that their brain is simply, temporarily, incapable of doing even the simplest tasks. Stay dog-on-bone with them until they get better. They can do it. And only with your support.

CHAPTER XIV

LAKE PARADISE

Marilyn is one of those soul friends on my triage team who is also in the "To Hell and Back Club." That is, she's hit rock bottom. She knows the horror of the moments when you want to die as well as the depth of joy you feel when you emerge from that darkness and claim your life again.

It is June 2008, and we can swim again. Not just any swim, but the forbidden swim across the lake where it's illegal to even dip. The only safe time to go is before 6:00 a.m. The town recreation department officials begin their patrol at seven. By the time they do their rounds, we are out and dry and dressed like any other upstanding citizens.

It had been a grumpy, whiny, chafing night for me and, knowing the elixir of this lake called Paradise, my soul had led my body up before dawn to join Marilyn for our ritual morning immersion.

Marilyn's house sits just above the lake facing east and floods with the sunrise flickering across those waters. On this near solstice morning, sunrise is at 5:00 a.m. and the air is still chilly. A pink mist is rising off the lake, partially obscuring and partially revealing the mountains on the far side. I am silenced by the gentle, loving beauty of this place. As Marilyn likes to say, quoting a song from Jennifer Berezin, we are "returning to the mother of us all." The tears that formed behind my eyes merge with the water as we dip, and my raw edges melt. I am at once free, clean, clear, strong, and grateful.

Marilyn first invited me on her sacred, forbidden swims a year ago. We had known each other casually for years, then had gotten closer when I became a loyal student in her Tuesday morning yoga classes. At six months of round-the-clock nursing the twins, I had given myself this class to restore my body to some degree of strength and flexibility. This also gave my brain and soul a two-hour break from double-infant exhaustion.

Marilyn's class was an oasis in time. Simply upon entering her yoga studio, I could feel my heart slow and my breath expand. Her voice, at once rhythmic, gentle, and wise, was a balm for my weary soul. I'd leave there feeling restored enough to take on the rest of the day.

When Marilyn's marriage ended, the breakup triggered a flood of old wounds and a tailspin, which, in turn, triggered her genetic predisposition for mental illness. I'd felt honored that she confided this in me, even though she is a genuinely private person. I had been surprised to hear that my seemingly flawless-in-temperament yoga guru could suffer such a fall. Having been there myself, I felt compassion for her and prayed that she'd find her way up and out. After two years of struggle, when Marilyn finally hit on the right combination of supplements, therapy, and diet to find health again, she described herself as one of the women in the "To Hell and Back Club." We knew a few others.

Later, when I took my free-fall descent, Marilyn recognized the journey. She'd invite me on a hike, one of the few activities I found comfort in. At some point she would stop in her tracks, lock my gaze with her magnificent green eyes (now watering), and say, "You will heal, Sara. I know you will. I've been there, too, and I'm back. Even more joyful and grateful than before. I know it's hard for you to hear this now, but I promise, you will get better."

I didn't believe her. So many well-intentioned friends had endeavored to reach me with kind words but could not. Their lifeline was tethered to a buoy that floated on the surface, but I lived at the bottom of the blackest sea, where no one, no matter how loving or brave, could travel to rescue me, except maybe Joe. Merciless guards blocked those gates, and they were not going to leave their post any time soon. I was not going to get better. I was happy that Marilyn had recovered, but her story had no relevance to mine.

After twenty-two years of teaching yoga, Marilyn abruptly announced one day that she'd decided to retire. "I just know the time has come to do something different," she said, shocking the class with the news. She would work at a friend's organic facial products factory, brewing elixirs for the skin. Marilyn was ecstatic with the change. I was devastated. What would I do without this one place of refuge? She must have known, because as we rested in the final pose of the class, Shavasana, she whispered to me, "I'll still meet you for yoga, once a week."

It was a hot June day in 2007 when we met at her house for the first time, and yoga morphed into the illicit dip and swim. My body experienced some relief in water, but my mind was still tormented. Drying off, Marilyn asked me, "Name three things you love about yourself." I could not come up with one. Instead, I began a litany of my failings—lazy, depressed, unemployed, suicidal, bloody, absent from my kids, cold to my husband. Marilyn had known me as somewhat of a dynamic leader in our extended circle. Now she was witnessing for the first time how far down I'd slid.

We continued our yogic swims through that summer. As the Lamictal began to take effect, I slowly regained consciousness, perspective, and health. When the lakes froze and the trails turned to snow, our outdoor romps shifted to match the seasons, cross-country skiing, snowshoeing, and skating.

Now June again, just one year after my first visit to Lake Paradise, I am struck by the beauty of this sunrise scene. And the tear of awe in my eye is not only for the majesty of creation, but also for the memory of where I've been. I can feel this morning scene, absorb its beauty, love myself in it, and even feel exalted that I've motivated us to rise on a brisk dawn. My bond with Marilyn is stronger now, not only because we love this crazy illegal sunrise dip into the "mother of us all," but also because we share membership in the women's "To Hell and Back Club." And now that we're back, we know that the other knows just how sweet it is to feel gratitude for this mist and this sun and this water and the love of this friend.

Because of her personal struggle with mental illness, Marilyn also understood, unlike the gurus who err on the side of arrogance, that while yoga is a wonderful practice for health and vitality, it is no match for a genuine biochemical brainstorm like bipolar II. For some, the road to hell is paved with a dogmatic attachment to alternative therapies. Marilyn gave me a model of a woman I respected for her personal discipline as a quintessential yoga practitioner, who nevertheless possessed a genetic brain imbalance. Her embodied understanding was a therapeutic comfort, what my colleague Cliff Barry would call a "shame-lifter."

"It's not your fault, Sara, it's just chemistry," Marilyn said. "There is no shame in taking medicine for this. I do. I got better; you will too."

And if Marilyn couldn't be cured by yoga, who could?

Here's what I want to tell you about yoga, meditation, diet, exercise, body work, and all great practices of holistic healing: they are wonderful but they do nothing to touch the bipolar brain at its worst. Believe me, I've tried, heroically applied, even obsessively practiced these therapies in the hope and prayer that they would heal me. I believed drugs were a crutch that I did not need, and that by force of will and discipline I could out-maneuver the depression.

My bookshelf attests to this. Here are some of the titles: *Yoga for Depression*; *Stop Depression Now (with Sam-e)*; *The Rhodiola Cure*; *Depression: Cured at Last!* (with diet and herbal supplements); *The Kabbalistic Path to Ending Depression*; *The Feminine Brain (and How to Heal It)*; *Perimenopause and Depression (and Holistic Means of Recovery)*; and *The Omega 3 Cure*.

You get the picture. Many were written by MDs or PhDs with impressive research credentials but zero real-world experience with the disease. Others were authored by alternative practitioners with orthodox—and sometimes self-convinced views—about the one true path to wholeness, each advocating their method as curative and superior.

For the depressed person being pummeled in the midst of a brainstorm, these approaches offer the proverbial "any port in a storm." You grasp for a lifeline. You pray that this is the one path you've not tried that will be the key to your unique chemistry. You are susceptible to snake oil and voodoo. You are easy prey for the predatory salesman of the cure-all supplement. Many of these betray the Hippocratic oath and end up perpetrating more harm than good.

Take, for example, the self-proclaimed healer I mentioned earlier, whom I'll call "Paula," who made her living as a psychic. A close friend said Paula was a powerful healer and insisted that I see her. Paula charged me three hundred dollars for an hour and proceeded to tell me in a shaming and condescending tone that drugs were evil products of profit-driven Big Pharma, that family genetics could be overcome through meditation, and if I just stopped eating sugar and "opened my crown chakra," I would be cured. Spoken with the utter arrogance of someone who has zero personal experience with this disease.

You must be painfully ignorant of the chemical dynamics of a bipolar brain to speak in these kinds of universal platitudes and then have the nerve to collect three hundred dollars for your harmful opinions.

You are also easily the victim of caring but ill-informed friends. Each trying to help. Each with their own theory of wholeness. Many of them highly skilled in their own domains, but ignorant when it comes to the intricacies and vulnerabilities of the bipolar brain. I live in a part of the country that is a mecca for alternative health approaches. My friends are gifted (even world-renowned) naturopaths, homeopaths, acupuncturists, Thai massage practitioners, macrobiotic nutritionists, craniosacral therapists—you get the picture. One credits her diet with curing breast cancer. Another shows how his therapy healed a stroke victim. A third depicts the correlation between massage and stress reduction. They are credible. They've been successful. They love me, see me in pain, and want to help. And sadly, they were all wrong. What they were offering could not touch the biochemical storm in my brain.

It took me twenty-five years of exploration to figure this out. I wish I'd known sooner.

I'm not saying that these approaches aren't valuable. For a healthy person seeking optimal vitality, they are essential and wonderful. The silver lining of research into and practice of these paths is that when my brain is functioning, I'm one of the healthiest sixty-year-olds you'll find on the block. My primary care doc, upon performing an annual physical two years ago, pronounced me the healthiest fifty-eight-year-old in his practice. Perfect scores on blood pressure, pulse, respiration, etc. I figure if I can keep my head on straight, I'll be going strong at one hundred.

A lot of this is thanks to good genes—my parents looked great in their eighties—and I believe it's also due to decades of daily yoga practice, eating locally grown organic foods, doing morning meditations, and prayers. My devotion to these practices borders on the religious because I know that they are key to maintaining my mental health. And now that I've researched more about bipolar II, I've learned that along with establishing a steady sleep pattern (to bed close to dark, up with the sun) and a good dose of outdoor aerobics, they are essential to maintaining my health. I am grateful to have this knowledge and these teachers in my life. And knowing the risk of what's on the other side for me, you bet I am devout in my dedication.

But I've also learned that none of these practices can cure my bipolar II brain when it is triggered into its downward cycle. And as clinical psychologist and writer Kay Redfield Jamison says in her book *An Unquiet Mind*, "I have finally accepted that in addition to all these health practices, I need the medicine to keep me healthy."

I've finally moved beyond acceptance to utter gratitude: the-on-your-knees kind. When I witness the life of my sister-in-law's brother, a former soccer star and scholar destroyed by schizophrenia, another brain disease for which there is no good cure at present, I'm clear that, here but for the grace of G-d, go I.

The medicine is a gift. If, heaven forbid, the post-peak-oil-economic-breakdown-Armageddon does come, I'm going to find a band of fellow vigilantes to join me in occupying the factory that makes Lamictal. That stuff is saving my life.

CHAPTER XV

COMING OUT,
ENDING THE STIGMA,
LIFTING THE SHAME

I'm writing this partly because it's healing for me to tell my story and partly because I wish I had found a guide like this, written from the inside, when I was in my darkest hours. Someone who had a brain like mine telling her story of devastation and renewal, death, and resurrection. Someone who could speak to me as an insider to give me comfort and hope and lift some shame off my sunken shoulders. I'm hoping this story will help someone like me, someone who is suffering alone in the darkness and sees no light at the end of the proverbial tunnel.

None of the "expert" books and printouts that occupy more than three long bookshelves in my bedroom really described my experience or showed me a way out. Except for one. I've mentioned it before. *An Unquiet Mind* by Kay Redfield Jamison is a brilliant, poignant, painful, and ultimately redemptive memoir of Dr. Jamison's struggle with her own brain disease, bipolar I. The book comes close to describing my experience of what it feels like to have a bipolar brain, and it really helped me.

Jamison is an academic superstar, an All-American beauty, a magnetic personality, and a wild manic depressive. She is also an esteemed psychopharmacologist from Johns Hopkins University, so she can speak of the disease from both personal and highly clinical perspectives. The book reads like high drama. In my most depressed state, when I had difficulty concentrating, I was able to get through it.

For me, the most impactful piece of Jamison's writing is her love-hate relationship with medication. At first, she refuses to take it. Has wild manic binges of spending, sex, and sleepless nights. Wreaks havoc in her life. Then gets on lithium. Finds that it stabilizes her, but also takes the color out of her days. She misses the highs. Comes back off the drugs, reasoning that she doesn't need them, that they destroy her creativity and *joie de vivre*. Then comes the inevitable crash—days and weeks of being unable to leave her house, her mood excruciatingly painful. Finally, after years of this devastating cycle, she comes to terms with the fact that she must take lithium. That it is a lifesaver, and that she is on a collision course with destruction without it. She finds a dose of the drug low enough to allow her creativity to flow, but strong enough to eliminate her manic-depressive cycle. She finally finds equilibrium, peace, relationship, sobriety, and professional achievement.

I have never experienced the highs Jamison describes and have none of the classic manic symptoms. When feeling at my best, I am more energetic, optimistic, and full of life's wonder than the average middle-aged white woman. The gratitude for life I experience is a blessing. Since I don't experience the mania Jamison describes, her story is not mine. In fact, her sickness is easier to diagnose than bipolar II because it shows a classic pattern of the manic depression that has responded well to lithium for decades. What did resonate with me was Jamison's struggle to accept the need for medication in her life. That she had a chronic disease and needed to treat it as such. It took me a quarter of a century to accept this and to feel grateful that effective medicines are available.

My sister-in-law's schizophrenic brother is not so lucky. No drugs have been found yet that cure schizophrenia, and this former All-American scholar-athlete lives half the life he might have had. He is unable to hold a job, or marry, or do anything beyond menial tasks for himself. There but for the grace of G-d and some mysterious medicines go I. It's a chemical equation, and I'm lucky the chemists have found something that works to heal my brain.

Well-meaning professionals, friends, family, and other experts can get it wrong. As my lovely and wonderful nurse midwife, Liza, said when hearing of my bipolar status, "You get depressed because you don't have the energy to do things, right?"

"No," I explained. "You're depressed because your brain doesn't work. You can't add. You can't focus. You can't cook. The prospect of doing dishes is overwhelming. Not only because you are sucked dry of the energy to do them, but also, and more importantly, because your brain has no way of figuring out how to accomplish a task this complex."

"This is not a 'mental health' question. It's not a question of being sad or of unresolved issues with your mother. Your brain simply doesn't work. It's missing some essential nutrient, or salt, or other undiscovered element essential to its healthy function. As others have said, it's like insulin for a diabetic. Essential for life. Not something to be ashamed of."

"You've got to write about this," Liza said. "You can help people appreciate the distinctions. I certainly never 'got' this before."

Dr. Perlman got the right diagnosis because he was astutely aware of the subtle distinctions and had seen how well Lamictal worked in others with bipolar II. He was sure of his diagnosis because of my family history (with my mother successfully on lithium for more than three decades), and because Lexapro had made me manic. The puzzle was complete in his clinical judgment, and he was right.

Six months into feeling well, I asked Dr. Perlman how the drug works. "What's the mechanism?"

"We have no idea," he said, "we just know it does."

What is different in the brain between unipolar and bipolar depression that makes different medicines have such dramatically different results? What is the genetic and biochemical brain pattern that trips a switch for the bipolar II person and causes the system to crash? How do the drugs work, in a contemporary metaphor, to reboot that system? No one seems to really know. It's as if the mysteries of how the human brain works are one of the final frontiers for biology and science. As vast a territory perhaps as the universe is wide.

I'm left with some intellectual curiosity about all this, but mostly a profound feeling of relief and gratitude. Life remains mysterious, and this brain of mine is one mystery I might not crack in this lifetime. Meantime, thanks to the right chemical equation, my life is back. More precious than before and with a recognition of how vulnerable and fragile our human body-minds are.

This morning I am writing in my friend Leah's majestic studio. It's set in the woods with large picture windows revealing vistas of the mountains to the north and west. Maple trees with their fresh green leaves sway in the breeze. With hot tea, a good friend, a morning hike and chat behind us, it is a pleasure to write in silence, hearing only the steady sound of fingers tapping.

A year ago in 2007, this was not possible. My fingers would bleed on the keys. I had no capacity to focus. And though I tried to write because it had been a form of catharsis, expression, and creativity for me in the past, I would fall asleep at the computer. With memory impaired, word recall was excruciating and exhausting. I'd feel embarrassed and incompetent at the end of our writing circles, once a source of community and connection, which ended with me having nothing to share.

All the sweeter it is to sip tea and write this morning. I am struck by a conversation I had earlier this week. I am still involved in the financial dispute with the coauthors who refuse to honor our contract, which clearly prescribes the royalties be split. I've finally consulted a lawyer, who says I have an airtight case and that "any court of law in the country would dismiss" my coauthors, whose sole argument is, "We don't believe in contracts."

My friend Lynne says, "I wonder what curveball they might throw at you. I bet their lawyer will say, 'She's mentally ill.'"

Images of Thomas Eagleton's run for the vice presidency in 1972 cross my mind. He was "outed" as having gone through electric shock therapy, and that was the end of his bid. Yet he went on to complete more than two decades of distinguished service in the Senate.

Or, for a Hollywood version of craziness, there's *One Flew Over the Cuckoo's Nest.* Crazy people, people who suffer from depression or bipolar I or II, lose all credibility.

Suddenly, I am grateful that I did not choose ECT. Or the psych ward, or the outpatient psychiatric clinic. I'm grateful that millions of Americans are on an antidepressant and practically everyone has a cousin or brother on one, even if they themselves are not. I'm grateful that I've never shared my bipolar II diagnosis with my coauthors, so they can't use it against me. And I'm grateful that this text is not yet published. When it is, I can use a pseudonym if I choose.

Then the injustice of all this strikes me. Why should I have to stay in the closet when the DNA for this disease is in my genes? This is not something I've chosen. Or brought on myself because of bad behavior. On the contrary, I've been diligent about preventive health and self-care. Ask my friends, who marvel at my discipline when it comes to diet, exercise, meditation, prayer, community. A year ago, through absolutely no fault of my own, I could not have written this paragraph.

The term "mental illness" evokes images of crazy people who, through some flaw of character, have created their own miserable destinies. People with mental illness might receive sympathy from their successful, healthy peers: *They were victims of abusive or neglectful parenting, or there were drugs or violence in their homes growing up, or they never got a break.* Or they might receive contempt: *These people are incapable of being productive citizens.* Or they might be screens for the projection of our own fears. *They are scary, potentially violent people who should be locked up and kept away from us and our kids.* The term "mental illness" conjures up all these images, and people branded with the label are today's lepers.

I assert that bipolar depression II is misunderstood when we refer to it as a "mental illness." If I had a knife in my liver, you wouldn't ask me about my issues with my mother; you'd stop the bleeding. If I had a thyroid problem, you'd treat it. If my brain has a physical malfunction that prevents it from operating properly, don't look only for childhood trauma, even though it might be significant, because that won't be sufficient to heal me. Find me a diagnosis and a treatment that addresses the physical nature of how this ailment impacts the brain.

This shift in mental models and how we view this disease is critical to alleviating the shame and humiliation those who carry it suffer. On an individual level, if I think the disease is all my fault, I invest countless hours and dollars analyzing my personal failings, my dysfunctional family, my life mistakes. On a therapeutic level, some psychological professionals collude with this approach, which fits their world view, and helps make their livelihood. On a policy level, those who carry the gene for bipolar are discriminated against in their relative lack of access to medical treatment and the insurance to cover it. Again, nobody questions that health insurance should cover heart disease. Why do we draw the line at brain disease?

This is not to say that all emotional therapy is misguided in the treatment of bipolar II. I have benefited enormously from skillful and compassionate guides in this domain. I have also seen the healing power of other healing approaches, including Shadow Work, and attest to their value, especially for the millions of people in our country who are victims of violence, sex abuse, addictions, and any "ism."

The point is that emotional and behavior modification therapies should not be viewed as sufficient for people suffering from a brain disorder. While they might benefit from therapy for other circumstances in their lives, no therapy alone can heal a bipolar brain anomaly. Period. Though they are inextricably linked, let's not equate the emotional domain of the psyche with the physical domain of the brain.

My friend Rosie, who has just read what I wrote above, comments, "Yeah, but it cuts both ways. Think of all the people who've been drugged up when they really needed good therapy." And Mara, an elementary school librarian who knows the demographic, adds, "And all the 'ADHD' kids on Ritalin. The overuse of that drug is criminal."

I imagine that there are millions of people on Prozac right now who really don't have physical brain malfunctions and really do need some good therapy instead of drugs. The psychiatrists-turned-salespeople on the pharmaceutical companies' payrolls encourage this trend. Who knows where to draw the line in the pool of those suffering from various types of depression, what percentage of people are depressed due to emotional trauma, and what percentage are depressed because of a genetic brain malfunction?

Perhaps it's impossible to tell. Or perhaps research dollars dedicated to addressing this question in a credible scientific manner could shed some insight on the subtle interplay between physical and emotional triggers in brain chemistry. Perhaps if we removed the stigma that the term "mental illness" brings, along with its connotation that the mentally ill person is somehow to blame for their troubles, more research dollars would be allocated to understanding the variety of brain functions and patterns.

Ultimately, I can only speak what is true for me. I spent too many years under the influence of the wrong concept—that my struggles were strictly psychological, spiritual, and emotional. I like to think I have some control over my destiny. When I was younger, this led me to refuse to believe that I had "the family disease" or that my struggles were a genetic thing that I could not conquer through force of will. If I only practiced an organic ideal of behavioral perfection, I could overcome any chemical vicissitudes of my brain. I was excessively disciplined in this approach, trusting that if I did it right, all the time, I could dodge the depressions I'd experienced earlier.

But this game of "dodgeball" exhausted me. It's a relief to know and accept that there is a chemical component that controls when my brain works and when it doesn't work. It's a relief to surrender to this truth: I do not fully control my world. Nor, for that matter, do I control the world. As Dr. Perlman said, "You have a chronic genetic illness. Lots of people do. You'll learn to live with it. Thankfully, in your case, there's a treatment.

Mental illness in general and bipolar specifically need to come out of the closet. For this reason I finally chose to use my real name for this book to lift the shame off myself and others. Maybe if we see more examples like me, a healthy and blessed woman with a lovely husband, children, home, friends, work, and a bipolar II brain pattern, stereotypes of the mentally ill will begin to shift.

Gay bashing and hate crimes are still perpetrated against homosexuals in this country. Yet, for the most part, and certainly in metropolitan areas, they are safer "out of the closet" than in years past. Indeed, the likes of Ellen DeGeneris and Pete Buttigieg have made it virtually hip to be gay. The Americans for Disabilities Act has made it illegal to discriminate against people with physical disabilities.

When Betty Ford spoke out as First Lady and said publicly that she had breast cancer, she paved the way for millions of women to say that they, too, struggled with this disease. There's no longer social judgment placed on diabetics for taking insulin. So why the stigma that comes with the label "manic depression?" A stigma that may be worse for people of color with mental health challenges, people who are often demonized for their differences. Why, despite scientific research that suggests that the disease is passed through the genes, did I seriously consider writing this book under a pseudonym? Why am I afraid to tell my client, who respects, even adores me, and just yesterday gave me the honor of asking me to lead his multimillion-dollar foundation, that I have bipolar II?

It is time to bring this brain dysfunction out of the closet. On top of the vicious wild card that life has dealt us in managing this disease, we should not be forced to take on a mantle of social shame. Naming our experience in all its brutality and ruthlessness will be a gift to others who suffer alone. It is essential that we feel safe enough to come out and articulate the paths we've bushwhacked on our way to wholeness and to light a torch on a moonless night to guide others on their way out of the darkness.

I am grateful to Ted Kennedy's son Patrick, the former Rhode Island congressman, for his courage in coming out as bipolar and fighting for legislation in support of the rights of those who carry this disease. His powerful position and name make this move a great step forward in removing the stigma.

In retrospect, I feel no disgrace, no dishonor, no shame. On the contrary, I see a spirit and soul with tenacity, perseverance, and courage to withstand the onslaught of a relentless attack, and keep going, hour after excruciating hour. From the perspective of a survivor, I bless the bravery and heart of that Spirit. Every night when I take the medicine that saves me, I bless the scientists tirelessly working in some windowless lab who came up with this cure and everyone else who dedicated themselves to bring it to my door: the manufacturer, the marketer, the doctor, the therapist, my sister, my friends; yes, even those pharmaceutical reps with integrity. All of them. I know that those who witnessed and loved me through this, honor me for my survival. But still, I worry about that lawyer who might exploit an anachronistic prejudice. It's time to make this kind of discrimination history.

CHAPTER XVI

DRUG WARS

A year after my recovery, what friends call my "brilliance" is back. My intellectual "database," as my friend and colleague Jannie refers to it, is back. My patience is back, as is my humor.

All of these are miracles for which I'm grateful daily. All are gifts I'll need this day to deal with my personal "drug war." I know how essential my meds are to my recovery. I'm not about to risk messing around with alternatives, generics, or skipping doses.

In one day in August, I deal with seven, count them, seven entities to get a prescription filled. We have a new insurance company with new rules. One says we can no longer get our medicine at our local pharmacy: We must get it through their mail order service. I learn what this means when, as I've done every month for the past thirteen, I try to fill my scrip, for twenty-five dollars, without a hitch at my local CVS.

"That will be $360."

"What?"

I do the math—at this rate a year's supply will cost me $4,320.

"Your insurance company has denied coverage. You'll have to take it up with them."

"But I've been covered every month for a year."

"I can't help you. You'll have to call them."

"These meds are essential."

"Sorry, next!"

Along with my other personal attributes that had returned came a genetic off-the-charts persistence and a lack of comprehension of the word "no" when applied to me.

"I need to talk to your supervisor."

Three supervisors later, I get to Charles.

"Thank you, Charles, I appreciate your time. Here's the deal: I can't afford to miss a day of my scrip. The insurance company is denying it. I'll deal with them, but I need you to fill it in the meantime."

Charles looks left and right. "I don't see why I can't give you a few days to tide you over." He puts a handful of pills in a container, and hands them across the counter.

I look him in the eye. "Charles, you're a good man. Bless your heart and your family." I walk out of there smiling. There are decent people who do good things despite bureaucracy.

When I get home and look more closely the next morning, I find that the pills are some unrecognizable shape and color. Alarmed, I call Charles.

"He's not in today."

"Well, can I speak to another pharmacist, please."

"Hello, can I help you?"

"Thank you. I take Lamictal and when I got home yesterday I found some strange-looking pills in my CVS container. I think there's been a mistake. Could you check that out, please?"

"I'll look at your chart. I see you've been given the generic version. They look different."

"But I need Lamictal. I know it works and I don't want to take any chances."

"I'm sorry, you'll have to take that up with your physician."

OK, breathe. I still have two days' supply of Lamictal left, there's time.

"Hi, Dr. Perlman, thanks so much for returning my call so quickly. Our new insurance company is giving me generics, and I don't want to screw around."

"That's fine, I'll fax a note saying, 'no substitutions' over there right away."

"Thank you so much. I'm sorry you've got to spend your valuable time dealing with insurance companies."

"Don't worry. It's no problem; we do it all the time now."

A friend had a psychotic break recently and I'd referred him to Dr. Perlman. Unfortunately, Dr. Perlman's practice was full, and he couldn't see him. I wonder how many more people in crisis could be served if Dr. Perlman did not have to spend his precious time faxing insurance companies.

Back to the present moment. Relieved that my travails are over, I go on with my day, figuring I'll stop by CVS after work.

"Hi, prescription for Schley, please."

"That will be $183 for 14 days."

Apparently, I got the right meds this time, but the cost has gone up: $4,396 for a year.

I spend three of the next twenty-four hours on the phone with seven entities and twice that number of customer "service" agents. They include the patient (me), the doctor, the pharmacy, the employer, the employer's insurance company, the insurance company's mail order company, and the mail order company's pharmacy.

Scenes from Michael Moore's movie *Sicko* flood my consciousness. What if I was as sick as I was a year ago? Then, without help from friends who had the stamina to fight, I never would have had the presence of mind, the patience, the negotiating skills, the pit-bull persistence, and the chutzpah to pull it off.

"Kathy, I'm glad you called, here's what's up. I've spent two days on the phone with seven entities and several people from your company all telling me conflicting things. I'm still nowhere near receiving my essential medicines. I'm a vice president at the Fortune 100 company that contracts your company's services and my next call is to our CEO to tell him why we should drop you. You're a nice person, and I wouldn't want to see you lose your job."

OK, this was stretching the truth—a lot. Not something I'm usually comfortable doing. Joe holds the insurance policy and is the VP of a small subsidiary of the Fortune 100 company, but what the heck, a life is at stake here.

"I'll get right on it."

Within five minutes Kathy calls back.

"I'm so sorry for the inconvenience, Ms. Schley. Your brand name Lamictal will be shipped out today. I'm going to waive the shipping fee. In the meantime, I've authorized your pharmacy to give you fourteen days of the medicine at no additional charge."

Now that's service.

"Thank you so much, Kathy. You've been a great help. Is there anything else we need to do to make sure this goes off smoothly from now on?"

"Your doctor needs to fax a new prescription in two months and every time he sends in a prescription or renewal he needs to write 'no substitutions' in the order. Other than that, you should be fine."

Traveling to CVS (a good twenty-two miles roundtrip) for the third time in as many days, I collect the medicine I need until the mail-order prescription arrives. I smile when I see the cost is $0.

Bad news: genetic brain dysfunction. Good news: genetic bulldog tenacity. Given I've got the first, it's a damn good thing I've got the second. Clearly, something's wrong with this picture when a person with mental health issues must jump through this many hoops, even when they're blessed with a job in the family that provides insurance, to get the medicine that saves their lives. Like I said, what would happen if I'd really been sick and didn't have enough medicine at home to tide me over?

I know we must pay trillions of dollars to maintain our status in the US as the biggest military presence on the globe, but sarcasm aside, can't we find the sanity, the goodwill, the political skill, and the public policy to fix this broken system?

That night, when I swallow the elixir that saves my life, I give an extra nod of gratitude for all the gifts and persistence it took to get this medicine to my door. Yet I'm appalled by the dysfunction in our health-care and insurance systems that requires someone with a PhD in persistence to get medicine. I hope it's easier for the next person who is sick and desperately needs relief.

CHAPTER XVII

PHOENIX RISING

Jim Head was the antiprofessor—young, cool, charismatic, and infamous on campus. In 1981, when I took his course, "Earth, Moon and Mars" (we called it "Earth, Wind and Fire" after the famous band) he was known as the geologist who had trained the NASA astronauts who walked on the moon. He had real moon rocks, which he'd been given as souvenirs by his buddies, on display in his office.

In Jim's class, we learned equations for gravity and mass that explain why the Earth is able to retain its atmosphere and water, one of the essential conditions that allowed life to emerge on this planet. The moon, by contrast, does not have enough mass for its gravitational pull to retain atmosphere and thus is not hospitable to life. Jim showed us dramatic movies taken on the moon, in black, white, and gray—no life there. We then viewed films of Earth from a distance and up close—waterfalls, mountains, rivers, deserts, people in all their diversity, cities, farms, African plains, a desert sky. The color and majesty of life on our small blue planet awed me. I remember thinking, despite the logic of the mathematics and science we'd learned, that this was all simply, exquisitely Divine. Call it what you like, G-d, Nature, Spirit, Creation, there is a force of beauty and infinite imagination that gifts us with life, with our lives.

This sense of gratitude and awe is what stays powerfully alive and present in me, having emerged, like the proverbial phoenix rising, from the ashes of depression. As I've shared, the word "depression" does not begin to capture the experience. It's more like that barren moon. The conditions for vitality are absent. Life cannot reside there.

By contrast, from the (winged) perspective of the phoenix, look at the miracle of life. This is not a cliché for me. This is real: The fact that I breathe, that I walk, that I make love, that I see color, that I laugh, that I articulate political views, that I love my children passionately, that I can recall the words to write this paragraph, that I revel in the woods with friends, that I can stretch my body and feel the muscles, that I plant seeds with my kids and then harvest the spinach and figure out how to make a spinach salad with tomatoes and goat cheese and mandarin oranges, that I actually like to wash and dry the dishes—because now I *can*. These ordinary things are anything but ordinary. I know that every moment I have breath and brain is a gift. All of creation is a miracle.

This is the gift of this disease. To be so fully cognizant of the miracle of our lives, moment to moment. To be blessed with gratitude and praise for creation. To offer that blessing to those we love. It is a generous perspective that comes from a place of having known utter defeat. When you return from that hell somehow intact, life is sweet.

I would never wish this disease on anyone; the pain is too intense and the risk of ruin too great. I pray every day that my children got their father's gene on this one and will never suffer the betrayal of their brains. I pray every day that my family legacy of bipolar ends with me.

Yet there are other gifts from having lived through the experience. I was a star kid who had everything going and sailed through life until age twenty-one. I didn't comprehend people who struggled and had little patience for them. Now, compassion reigns. I have been there, sister. I know, I know. I will not judge an addict again; I couldn't stop picking my bloody fingers even when it broke my kids' hearts to see me doing it. Patience with other people's breakdowns is also long. Behavior I would have once judged harshly as irresponsible or unreliable, I understand. I couldn't return phone calls or emails for months. Couldn't do my chores around the house. Couldn't show up with food or drink to a gathering. Couldn't be there for friends in need. So if you blow it one day, I'm going to figure you've got some challenge going on in your life that I don't know about. And I'll cut you some slack. Because I get it, I've been there.

Making money? Be generous in sharing it. Because there, but for the grace of creation, an amazing support network, and drugs that work, I'd require financial support too.

There is something else. My father was famous for his one-liners, such as, "Work, work, work, think later." "Nice guys finish last." "I got eleven battle stars in World War II." "There are two kinds of people in the world, those who say, 'I'd love to, but . . .' and those who say, 'What Time and Where?'"

The latter became the family mantra; you were accepted into the fold only if you were a "What Time." The highest praise for a friend was, "She's a real 'What Time.'" Though I still qualify as such most of the time, and like that kind of can-do, make-it-happen character, the tendency to separate the world into two types, one victorious and the other a "loser," did harm to my psyche.

Work, work, work, means never rest, rest, rest. As it turns out, this is disastrous for the bipolar brain. And by the way, it's not too good for most anybody else's body-mind either. Witness the stressed-out, crazed, computer, wireless, cell-phone-planted-in-the-ear-24/7 culture of infinite buzz we've got going. Like many, I'm susceptible to all that and could party on the adrenalin buzz of it until I crash and burn.

But I don't anymore. I know what's at risk the morning after that binge, and it's nothing a Bloody Mary and a cold shower can shake. It's as if I now have a cellular knowledge of how much action is too much and when I must give myself a break. Smell the lilacs. Feel the earth under my feet, inhale my daughter's freshly washed hair, let myself off the hook of my to-do list. BE. There is only this place, this moment. And no one (not even my internalized dad) can scare me into forgetting or betraying that understanding. Because I know my life is at risk. I won't do that to Joe and my kids if I can help it.

It turns out that obsession with drive and external accomplishment, the compulsion to control, is simply not as much fun as another way of experiencing life. A way that you might call surrender, or going with the flow, or receptivity, or listening for what is emergent. I'm a beginner here, so I can't say too much about it. Other than that, it's a bit of an adventure, like canoeing downstream, curious to see what's around the next bend in the river. As the title song on a friend's CD goes, "Everything is unfolding, is unfolding perfectly." Increasingly, I'm finding delight in this way of being.

I don't mean to preach. Or sound as if I've got the spiritual truth, have been to Mecca and have found Enlightenment with a capital E. I'm just hoping to convey hope for you if you are struggling, and hope and patience and faith for those who love and pray for you. There is a stark beauty to this disease. There is a possibility of redemption from your cells to your soul.

If someone you love is suffering from a bipolar brain, it might be very difficult to keep frustration, judgment, and even condemnation at bay. "Why can't she just get her act together? I've made fifteen suggestions for activities for her to get involved in, therapists to contact, jobs to pursue . . . and she just sits there and does nothing!" "I've set out a daily schedule for him to get up out of bed, have some breakfast that I'll even prepare in advance for him, and go do things. He could volunteer for a community organization that does things he likes to do, do something helpful to others." "If he would just get a decent job, he'd be fine."

You might think she's spoiled, lazy, ungrateful, entitled, taking advantage of you. You might think you've been saintly with your generosity and still nothing's changed. You might feel your efforts have not amounted to anything.

All these feelings are understandable and fair. Still, they won't help you or your loved one. No matter how much you push your strategies, this thing is about brain chemistry. No strategy, no matter how brilliant, will touch it until the chemistry is addressed first. Though this step is essential, it takes time. As the best doctors will tell you, our knowledge of how the brain works is far from adequate to the task, and it is an art, not a science. There is a lot of guesswork involved on the part of practitioners as to what will work for each person.

The brain is as vast as the universe and equally uncharted. At this point, feeling well, I accept the mystery and simply say, "Thank You." Still, the day when science understands the brain so that these powerful drugs can be more precisely targeted and less of a dart game will be a blessing for all. Bottom line is that both the person suffering with the disease and those who love her must be excruciatingly patient.

My friend whose nephew committed suicide, having suffered with undiagnosed and untreated bipolar, has an urgent message to share: "You may want to believe it when a depressed person assures you that he or she would never commit suicide, never thinks about it. But believe it when they tell you they have no energy left, can't find the will to apply for jobs, to work; they just want to be able to get up out of bed in the morning and take care of themselves, cook their own breakfast (not even going so far as to go out and buy food). Believe it when a depressed person says they don't find anything interesting, even when they try—not art classes, not exercise, not anything, although they deeply appreciate visits from family and friends. Believe it when the depressed say they have no hope."

Meantime, if you are a primary caretaker, lover, or friend, get support for your own frustrations, grief, rage, or terror. Find a friend, a therapist, a support group, or all these things, and let them help you. Do everything you need to do to take care of yourself, body, mind, heart, soul, and spirit.

You are in it for the long haul; this is a marathon, not a sprint.

CHAPTER XVIII

THE SOLOIST

Joe and I had heard that the film *The Soloist* had stellar performances by Jamie Foxx and Robert Downey Jr., and since we had the rare treat of a Saturday night with a babysitter, we made a spontaneous choice to see the movie. It was an early spring night with a full moon on the rise and possibility in the air. We knew nothing about the plot of the film.

Downey Jr. plays the journalist Steven Lopez, who stumbles onto Jamie Foxx's character, Nathaniel Anthony Ayers Jr. Ayers is sitting on a downtown Los Angeles bench beneath a statue of Beethoven, mumbling unintelligibly at high speed about his love of music while playing an intoxicating melody on his two-string violin.

Ayers is homeless and drives a shopping cart full of junk. From the moment we meet Ayers on screen, I feel my heartbeat quicken. I'm awash in tears as his story unfolds. Convulsions of sobs come when we witness the moment his disease attacks his brain. At about age twenty, he is playing cello in the Julliard Orchestra with great joy and abandon, and deep connection with his colleagues. The joy in his inner being is palpable, and I hold my breath, intuiting the inevitability of what happens next. Indeed, in the next scene, playing the same cello in the same orchestra, he's suddenly attacked by a slew of voices, and is struck by overwhelming confusion. Inexplicably, he can't remember how to move the bow across the strings. Then we see him at home in his apartment, disoriented, in the fetal position, flailing, screaming.

I am there, suddenly transported to age twenty-one, experiencing the first time my brain betrayed me. Tears stream down my face as I watch Ayers's demise. This is me; I am at college unable to make sense of the professor's words, incapable of focusing on any text. Immobilized. Afraid of crowds and stores and friends. Yet craving contact. The bottomless free fall with no one "on belay" to catch him. I cannot give words to how terrifying this is. It's like some night-of-the-living-dead horror flick. Only I'm living its cruelty, measured in endless, minute by minute, hour by hour, day by day, minute by minute, day by day, hour by hour, day by day, week by week, minute by minute, time. Eternal damnation. For what cause?

Watching the film, I squeeze Joe's hand as hard as I can. I am *here*, Joe is *here*, and it is *now*, and I am *safe*. I am *happy*. Life is *good*. But tears are still flowing. Perhaps for the first time since my recovery, I am feeling the grief of years lost to this disease. Who would I be if it had not struck me down at the tender age of twenty-one? Would I have achieved more fame, more power, more wealth, more glory? Perhaps. All I know is that my life now is sweet, and I have earned a heart of compassion that a life of victory upon victory would not likely have given me.

Outside the theatre now, I'm still shaking and crying. Yet the moon is full, and I see its glory. Lilacs, my favorite flower, are at their peak. I stop to inhale their scent, sensing this will help ground me in the present. I am intoxicated by the smell. I feel Joe's hand in mine and let the love open my heart. It's true. I am OK. My brain is working; I can see, feel, and sense these gifts. I could easily have been the homeless, "mentally ill" person in the film. But I'm lucky. I have survived. I'm a survivor.

When we arrive home, the kids are asleep. It's the eve before Mother's Day, and I'm aware of how blessed I am to be the mother of these two magnificent souls. I kiss their heads, absorbing the perfection of this moment. I can feel this love; I'm alive and I'm OK.

In the film, a wise therapist explains to Steve Lopez that he might never be able to cure Ayers, but that friendship alone has been known to shift a victim's brain biochemistry. "Just show up," the therapist says.

I am still shaking. I look into Joe's chocolate brown eyes. The eyes of my friend, who showed up, day after day.

I have only two words for Joe tonight.

"Thank you."

CHAPTER XIX

WRESTLING BLESSING FROM THE DEMONS OF BIPOLAR II

Originally, I thought "Wrestling Blessing from the Demons of bipolar II" would be the subtitle for this book. I read the Bible as metaphor and mirror, with characters who teach us about our own lives.

In *Genesis*, Jacob wrestles with a powerful energy in the middle of the night and emerges with a new name, new power, and new blessing: "Jacob said to the one he wrestled, 'I will not let you go until you bless me.' And the Wrestling One said, 'I will give you a new name, Israel, G-d wrestler, for you have wrestled with me and with G-d and prevailed.' Jacob called the place 'The Face of G-d' for he had seen G-d face-to-face, and his life has been saved."

In the next scene, he meets his twin brother, Esau, the hunter whose birthright he has stolen. Jacob fears for his life, but he prays for forgiveness, "falls on his brother's neck, kisses him and they wept." Jacob then says to Esau, whom I see as the dark part of himself, "I have seen the face of G-d in you."

Jacob wrestled with a formidable energy and emerged with a new name and new strength, with which he asked for and received forgiveness. Love is what remained.

It is hard to imagine there could be any blessing in wrestling with the brutality of bipolar II. Yet having emerged from this near-death struggle, I've learned that there is. I hope my story has shown you there are gifts after the long night of wrestling, when the dawn finally emerges and light returns to you.

A French film called *A Secret* is set in post-Holocaust Paris. We see the sadly familiar and eternally horrifying images of Auschwitz—mountains of shoes and emaciated bodies bulldozed into the ground. The protagonist has never met his brother Simon, a captivating seven-year-old who has perished there along with their mother. The family has kept these deaths a secret from the younger brother, but eventually he has stumbled onto the truth. In the film, revealing the secret is cleansing and healing, and an opening for all.

My family has its own secrets. We knew that my grandfather had gone through electric shock in the 1950s, but never heard the details surrounding it. Outside of the family, the only thing friends and colleagues know is that my grandfather was a model citizen and leader of his community. My mother never told her parents, her siblings, or any of her friends about her own suicidal depressions. We never speak of them outside the family either. When Mom went through electric shock treatments at seventy-nine, it was something she hid from friends. Bipolar disease is cloaked in shame; we don't speak about it.

But truth heals. Telling our stories lifts the shame.

In November 2013, Israeli and American genetic researchers Ariel Darvasi and Todd Lenca from The Feinstein Institute for Medical Research found that the genetic risk of bipolar disorder is higher in Ashkenazi Jews than in the general population. As soon as I learned this, I started to worry about it and prayed that I hadn't passed the gene to my own innocent children.

But I didn't give it much deeper thought until recently, when I was at a recertification event for Shadow Work, the Jungian-based personal healing experience that brought Joe and me together. Shadow Work leaders are expected to offer and receive a session at least once a year. When I was on the receiving end of the process, I decided to focus on the tension between my high-achieving professional self and my bipolar self, the part of me which has been incapacitated time after time.

The Shadow Work methodology is to create a kind of theatrical drama, using people in the room to represent parts of ourselves. The first part I chose was the visionary, successful, powerful professional. The person I chose to represent that part of myself was standing facing forward. And her line in the theatre piece was: "I am capable, powerful, and here to serve." Then came the part representing the bipolar depressions that devastate me. I placed this "actor" face down, behind the visionary professional with her hands hooked around the professional's ankles, saying in a sinister tone, "Wherever you go, I am coming with you." Behind her came someone lying down and holding the ankles of the second person, and then a player behind her holding her ankles, and on and on back through the ages.

The facilitator asked what I saw there. "These people on the ground," I said, pointing to the floor. "The first one is my bipolar self. Holding her ankles is my mother. Holding my mother's ankles is my grandfather. Behind my grandfather are ancestors going back to generations before in Europe. It is a chain of torture and agony." Taking a step back, I was struck by the image of scores of people lying on the ground who looked like fatalities of war.

From one view, the scene could be a family chain of victims of bipolar. From a different angle, they could be victims of the Holocaust. Knowing that bipolar runs in the Ashkenazi Jewish line, is it possible that through an unknown genetic mutation, we had absorbed two thousand years of genocidal oppression and internalized it? With that thought came a flood of tears and a wave of compassion for these people, my ancestors. It was not their fault that they had been murdered. It was not their fault that they had been suicidal. One emerged from the other. I'd always resented my genetic line for giving me this disease. Now, seeing the innocence of my ancestors, I could forgive them, and feel that forgiveness coming back to me, to lift the shame, tell the secrets, heal myself.

Though the field of epigenetics is young and controversial, there is evidence that trauma can be passed down through the genes. In an article in the *Atlantic*, "Inherited Trauma Shapes Your Health," (October 2018), Olga Khazan writes ". . . in 2016, Rachel Yehuda of Mount Sinai hospital and her colleagues found that Holocaust survivors and their children both had evidence of methylation on a region of a gene associated with stress, suggesting that the survivors' trauma was passed onto their offspring."

Ironically, I find some hope in this. If genes can be imprinted by trauma, couldn't they also be made whole through emotional, physical, and psychological healing?

A month before the Shadow Work˚ experience in 2009, I had been honored by two hundred people in my community in a ceremony that came to me as a surprise, and given the new name Eshet Hazon, Hebrew for "woman of vision." It was a blessing from the community for the leadership I'd offered in Jewish chanting, meditation, and prayer services over the last decade. As part of the ritual, people were invited by the rabbi to come up to me one by one and offer a blessing. Several of these friends were in tears, as was I, knowing that only eighteen months before I'd been suicidal with bipolar, and on the verge of becoming the third generation in my family line to receive electric shock therapy.

Jeff, an open-hearted soul who had come to my house on many occasions during those endless dark days simply to hold my hand and take me for a slow walk outside, cried with smiling eyes. "Tears of joy," he said. "It's a miracle." Both of us were mindful of the awe of this occasion, knowing the utter anguish I'd so recently emerged from.

It was a beautifully ironic turn of events when my former therapist Jennifer Brown called with a request. She'd been at the ceremony and attended the chanting prayer services I'd led over the years.

"Sara, would you help me lead a healing circle for Phyllis?"

"Of course," I said without hesitation. Phyllis is loved among many friends and was dying of cancer.

I was honored by the request. Jennifer had seen me at my darkest hour, and I believe she knew that having been there, I was capable of helping to lead others in an emotionally intense and painful time.

We worked closely together on the preparation of the service, Jennifer choosing poems and meditations, me choosing prayers and chants. A hundred and fifty beloved friends of Phyllis filled the room and created a magnificent circle of depth, love, and prayer. When it was over, Phyllis said it was the first time she had felt peaceful since her diagnosis months earlier. She felt loved by all of us. One by one, people approached Jennifer and me, and thanked us for the wisdom and warmth of the service.

But the feedback that was most powerful for me was from Marcia: "People told me that you had an exquisitely peaceful and compassionate presence that allowed them to feel safe and held in their feelings."

"Feisty, savvy, dynamic, high energy." These were all words I'd heard describing my leadership of large groups. But never "peaceful and compassionate." Two qualities of soul that I now aspire to as much as any worldly achievement.

I emerge from the darkness of the movie *Secret*, grateful that the sun has not yet set in the West. It is the edge of spring in New England and warm enough to breathe without burning your lungs. I meet Joe's eyes and see the eyes of our babies there. When we arrive home, they are sleeping the beatific sleep of the angels. It is beyond the comprehension of my mother's heart to know that only fifteen years before I was born, Hitler and his accomplices succeeded in murdering so many millions of children. I am overwhelmed with gratitude for Sam and Maya's lives—for their health, their innocence, their freedom, their safety.

In the movie, the deaths of Simon and his mother leave the father grieving their immeasurable loss. Joe and I, now in our bedroom, catch each other's gaze. We are survivors of a different kind, and my heart absorbs the blessing of this moment.

Predawn the next morning, I am the only one awake. I ascend to the small sanctuary above our bedroom and light the ten tea lights in windows North, South, East, and West. My teacher Shefa chants a wordless melody on a CD. As I stretch my body, I offer the ancient words of gratitude that are the Hebrew morning prayers. I remember that it is Friday and I do not work today, no two-hour commute. After getting the kids up, fed, and off to school, I will get to hike by the stream and then write with Leah. I will make challah and roast chicken, greet the bus at 3:00 p.m., and welcome friends for Sabbath dinner and celebrations. It is a beautiful day to be awake on this Earth, with this brain, this body, this life.

CHAPTER XX

MY SHOULDER,
MY MOM, MARTHA,
AND MENOPAUSE

After the conversation with my teens on the way to Florida, when I knew I would publish this book, I knew there was an additional chapter to write. In the decade since I'd finished the first version of the memoir, ending with the previous chapter, I'd had a relapse. I would have to tell the reader about what happened.

The first version had ended so positively. Twenty-five years into the disease, I'd finally gotten the right diagnosis and medication, and I was no longer held hostage by the terrorists of the mind. I was a free woman and dancing on the tables with joy.

Then, in 2015, three things happened at once:

(1) My mom received a terminal cancer diagnosis.

(2) I tore my labrum adjacent to the rotator cuff in my right shoulder, leading to excruciating pain that kept me from sleeping every time I got horizontal, which meant every time.

(3) I paddled full steam into the hormonal whitewater that is perimenopause.

These proved to be a one-, two-, three-punch. I was down for the count again with an incapacitating bout of bipolar like I hadn't experienced in close to a decade. I was devastated.

I had learned through the writings of Dr. Jim Phelps that lack of sleep contributes significantly to bipolar depression. As I've written earlier, this hit me when Maya was a baby with breathing issues that kept me up all night in a vigilant effort to keep her alive, administering albuterol through a nebulizer with relentless drone. To this day I get my own version of PTSD when I hear that sound. Muscles taut, eyes wide, heart pounding, ready for a high-speed chase to the ER. Chronic sleep deprivation had been a major contributing factor to my bipolar episodes when the kids were little. I knew sleep was crucial to my brain health, yet with pain shooting down my arm like rockets every night I just couldn't sleep.

Then there was the situation with Mom. My relationship with her was fraught, a tangled mix of fierce love, disappointment, sadness, and anger. As you know, she had suffered from bipolar episodes as long as I could remember, the first coming right after my birth. I loved my mom as children do. All the kids in our family did. But there was a greater intensity with me because of the identification I felt with her due to our shared experience of the disease. I couldn't feel this compassion when I was still raging at her in my twenties, but that anger softened over time, as I did my therapeutic work on my family of origin.

By the time I had my own children, my heart opened to my mother. My compassion for her grew as she became increasingly frail in her eighties. My siblings did not get the disease. As a result, they didn't understand our mother, me, or my growing empathy for her. I empathized with my mom's distress to a fault, sometimes to an unhealthy degree of enmeshment, as I had a visceral sense of what it was like to be inside her tortured brain. I knew the cruelty of that inside and out and wanted to climb under the covers of her mind to comfort her.

My disappointment and sadness came with the sense that my mom never found peace with the disease. Never found a way out. Her emotional turmoil was exacerbated by her feelings of being trapped in her marriage, and her proper upbringing that taught her never to vent her emotions. Thus, she would implode instead of explode, coming of age as she had before Gloria Steinem, Betty Friedan et al, created the woman's movement which might have given her a voice and the courage to free herself.

I remembered a women's circle that friends created the morning of my wedding. We sat in order of age, and Deborah, the leader of the moment, asked what advice the women had for me. My mom, as the oldest, went first and said something unmemorable. Probably, knowing her, it was pithy and witty, but scratched the surface. As we went around the circle, the sharing got increasingly deep.

After the last person, my mom asked if she could speak again. I held my breath, fearing sarcastic, cutting comments, for which she was known. She didn't like emotional sharing, and I figured she'd let us know. Instead, she stood up, and with hands trembling and voice shaking, said, "You girls don't know what you have. How precious this support is. If my generation of women had had this, things would have been different."

With the exception of my closest friends who knew my story, the women present couldn't know she was talking about how she'd struggled with mental illness in silence. Without any support. Keeping up appearances with her friends over coffee and cake and chatter about the kids. Never telling her own parents, despite knowing her father also suffered, and would have understood. I recall she did see psychiatrists for medication, but it seems she never received the emotional support from those professionals that could have helped. She certainly didn't tell any of her friends that she was on medication or what she needed it for.

As she began her dying process, with gastric cancer ravaging her (could this be about what she couldn't stomach?), I felt the pain of her loss. If only she'd had that support, what might have been different? She spoke to my sister and me constantly about her regrets—if only she'd kept a job, if only she'd been more disciplined, if only she'd left our father four decades ago. But she never did those things, and it tormented her. I felt her pain, felt powerless to help, felt sucked into the vortex of her distress, felt my own spiral downward. Even though I knew better, I was caught in my mother's spider web. Not that she would have ever wanted me to be, but there I was snagged, nonetheless.

As she was dying, my symptoms began to reappear, and I went to see Dr. Perlman. He wasn't worried. "Never underestimate the power of grieving," he said. "It's good to grieve the loss of your mother. The more you do that the better."

OK, but I was feeling myself spiral in that terrifying way, and I thought it was more than grief.

My friend Lynne, a midwife to the dying who had attended hundreds of deaths, said something similar. "Grief is like a computer program constantly running in the back of your brain. It sucks bandwidth and thinking power. Don't worry. You'll be back."

Eleven months to the day after my mom passed, I awoke from a dream. In it, we are sitting on the bed she shared with my father in my childhood home. When healthy, my mom was exquisitely elegant and impeccably dressed, but here she sits in her nightgown with her hair unwashed and the bed unmade. She keeps repeating the refrain, "I need to leave your father . . . I need to leave your father." I'm my present age in the dream, aware that she'd been dead for some months. "You can now, Mom," my dream self tells her.

"Who will get him his fresh cherries?" Mom laments.

"You don't have to do that anymore, Mom; you're free."

The scene changes to a massive ballroom. My mom is decked out in her most regal attire. She looks gorgeous, beaming. Her grandchildren, my little nieces and nephews, are there. There is festive music playing.

"Brookie, Em," I say, "take Gramma's hand and dance." They do and begin a circle dance. I am content to stand apart and watch, happy for my mother's happiness. I look up. To my delight, there are thousands upon thousands of people joining my mother in the dance. She is radiant.

"You know the Kabbalists believe that the soul graduates 'soul school' and rises up to the next level at eleven months," Joe says in the morning when I tell him the dream.

"She's on her way up. She wants you to know how well she's doing." I get chills of recognition. My mom is free from her suffering. Hallelujah.

But the comfort of this dream was over a year away. In the meantime, I was as stuck in the storm of my brain, as Mom had been so often in hers.

At the same time, I was smack in the middle of perimenopause. I'd never given it much thought, having never suffered from PMS or other hormonal imbalances. But this time at my annual OB exam with Dr. Linda Polonski, a wonderful doctor who'd known me for some twenty years, tipped me off that something might be whacky. I told her I didn't feel well. That my mom was dying. That I was beginning to feel depressed and was panicking about that.

"Where are you in your cycle now?" she asked.

"Well, you know I was twenty-eight days like clockwork for years. Now it's very inconsistent. Sometimes missing a month. Sometimes twenty-one days."

"Welcome to perimenopause," she said, not without compassion, as she jotted something down on her clipboard.

"Do you think that could be contributing to my mood?" I asked.

"Absolutely."

"What can I do about it?"

"Sadly, not too much. I'm afraid you just have to ride it out. You can talk to your psychiatrist to see if he wants to change your medication. But there's not much we can do on our end."

"How long will it last?"

"Hard to say. Can be three to five years."

WTF? I can't do this for three more years. I don't know if I can last three more months.

I embarked on my own research to see if there was anything to be learned about the correlation between perimenopausal women and bipolar. I did this in a panic, hungering for insight as to how to escape this time. A handhold in the rock crevice to rescue this climber, high up the cliff without a rope.

My sister was the first to find a clue.

"Check out the link I just sent you," Martha wrote late on a Thursday night.

Turns out there is a connection between perimenopause and bipolar. The research shows that a significant percentage of women who have been successfully treated for their bipolar brains may relapse when they go through perimenopause. The raging hormonal imbalance understandably correlates with an imbalance in brain chemistry. Now that we'd discovered that link, I'd be all set, right? Cure just right around the corner?

I felt momentarily buoyed by the fact that I was not alone. There must be a way to address this if so many women had suffered like me.

"And look where the research is being done!" said Martha enthusiastically. "There's a woman at UMass Medical in Worcester."

A flicker of hope. Not only is the UMass Medical Center just an hour's drive in the city of Worcester, Massachusetts, but also, my grandfather who had suffered from bipolar had been a civic leader in that city. In fact he'd chaired the fundraising committee that had won the contract to bring the medical center there in the 1960s. This was a big victory for the community the family was proud of. I felt his benevolent spirit blessing me from beyond the grave.

My sister rallied to help me get an appointment with the doctor leading the research. She tracked down her address, wrote her a note on my behalf, and set up a meeting. My friend

Annette volunteered to drive me, as navigating the route, finding parking, finding her office, simple tasks that I wouldn't blink at when healthy, were already way beyond my bipolar brain. My symptoms had spiraled into crisis mode that fast. Without their help I would have been too overwhelmed to start. We arrived at a stark floor in the hospital's psych department. No pictures on the walls, no warm receptionist, no clear direction as to where the doctor's office was.

When we found the office, there was a woman, much younger than I expected, behind a desk with a laptop. She barely looked up from the screen to greet us. Not the warm, nurturing type I was hoping for. I was glad Annette was by my side. At the same time, I did have a measure of hope. This woman was deeply immersed in the mysterious confluence of bipolar and menopause. Surely, she could help.

What followed was a two-hour interview in which the doctor asked me in-depth questions about my mental health history, going back more than three decades. She was very thorough. Again, I felt hopeful that the depth of her inquiry would lead to something positive. There was no small talk during this interview, no eye contact, and no acknowledgement of pain.

At the end of the second hour, she finally looked up from her computer.

"There's no doubt you are suffering from a relapse due to the impact of perimenopause and bipolar."

Pregnant pause. Good, I'm thinking. We know what I have.

"What should I do about it? Is there some hormonal treatment?"

"There's really nothing more that we can do for you beyond what you are already doing. You could talk to your psychiatrist about increasing your dose of Lamictal. I believe you could go up on that without harm."

What? Two hours of interviews, years of research, and that's it? Increase my existing Lamictal?

Deflated and in tears, I left the office with Annette and dragged myself back to the car. On the way home, I called Dr. Perlman. I'd told him I was going to see this doc. He had been encouraging and interested to learn about her research.

"She said to increase the Lamictal. That's it."

"We could do that," said Dr. P, "but as you know, an increase can correlate with loss of word recall and other unpleasant cognitive side effects."

The insidious and painful thing about having this disease is that you grasp at any handhold. And when you fail to land a grip, when the proposed strategy fails, your psyche crashes down, worse than before. Still, you can't stop trying. No matter how many times your hopes are dashed, you have to keep trying. After the kids were born, they were my main motivation to get better. Before that, I'm not sure what force tethered me by a single strand to life. I'm just glad it did.

Thankfully, physical cures I could manage, and my shoulder was getting better. My therapist had referred me to the miracle worker of PTs, Liz Dolby, with her upbeat, you-can-do-it style, and a series of specific exercises were working. The shooting pains slowly began to subside, and I started to get some sleep.

I was blessed to be there at that transcendent moment, along with my sister, when Mom took her last breath. I thought this transition might somehow release me from the grip of bipolar, as my mom had been released from her body; that maybe she would somehow bless me from the other side, as I knew she would be happy to do.

Instead, her death seemed to worsen my symptoms as I grieved her loss, dwelled on her endless regrets, and grieved that she had never been able to overcome what she called "the cruelest disease."

Several months passed. I struggled to force myself out of bed in the morning, to find my clothes, to remember to brush my teeth—the same insurmountable problems I've described before. Only somehow worse this time, perhaps because it was devastating to be back in this place after I thought I was finally free. It was the first time I'd been sick since the bipolar diagnosis and right meds in 2007. I was bereft that those strategies, which I thought would serve me forever, had stopped working. What to do now?

I don't recall what happened exactly, but I did feel better for a few months. Summer's long days, sun soaking, and swimming immersions were good medicine. I was beginning to feel myself again.

Then this.

My brother-in-law, Nat, called on my cell. Unusual for Nat to call, so I pick it up immediately.

"Hey Nat, what's going on?"

Nat usually opens his conversation with a quip or some silly news. This time he has a this-is-serious voice.

"Sara, Martha's at Falmouth hospital. She's had some sort of seizure. You'll want to get there fast."

"What happened?"

"She was driving with Andy (Dan's wife) and said she couldn't feel her left arm. Got out of the car and started shaking uncontrollably. Andy wisely took her to Falmouth hospital. They ran some tests and found a lesion in her brain. She's going by ambulance to Brigham and Women's." Brigham and Women's is one of Boston's top-notch hospitals.

"Oh no! Nat, tell her I'll be right there!"

I threw a few things in my car—cell phone, charger, wallet, change of clothes—and sped the twenty minutes to Falmouth hospital on Cape Cod, the closest one to us. When I arrived, Martha was in a wheelchair, with an IV, getting prepped for the ambulance. I ran to hug her, and she burst into tears. "I've been fine until I saw you," she said. I understood that meant that with me present, the only remaining woman in our original family, she was safe to feel her terror.

"It's OK, Honey," I said. "That's good. You gotta let it out."

Martha had been my rock during my previous depressions and in that moment I was hers. Our mother was gone and we were each other's lifeline.

When I'm well, I tend to be the lead dog, supporting, guiding, and coaching her. When I'm sick and at my most vulnerable and terrified, she is my first go-to. In this moment, I recognize my standard response in instances of triage: I get super calm, my brain shifts to rational and methodic, time slows down, and I'm present, reassuring, capable of making good decisions. The kind of person you want as captain in a storm.

"Brigham and Women's is the best. I'm gonna be tracking that ambulance right behind you, and I'll be there when you arrive. We've got this."

The story that unfolded over the next four weeks is worthy of another book, perhaps Martha's to write, about the drama and resilience of her brain. But since this book is about my brainstorm,

I'll keep it to this: Martha's lesion had to be removed via emergency brain surgery immediately after that Labor Day weekend by an exquisitely skillful surgeon I could kiss with joy. Despite the lesion being in what the surgeon called the "high real estate area" (this meant Martha risked losing the use of her right arm), she recovered 100 percent.

Then, just as we were exhaling and toasting with champagne celebrating Martha's successful brain surgery, we learned she would have to have a tumor in her lung removed just three weeks later. Emotional roller coaster. She was a rock star throughout all this, retaining an unshakable positive attitude, courage, and faith that awed me. No doubt that contributed to her recovery.

I maintained my triage mode of strength throughout this time.

"I feel like I've got my arms out in front of me in warrior stance, defending Martha from a Mack truck that's hurtling toward her," I told Joe. "I don't know how much longer I can sustain it."

"Sara, you know what's at risk. Make sure you take care of yourself."

"I know, I will."

Still, Martha's cancer coming so soon on the heels of my mother's death from cancer and my plunge into depression proved too much for my tenuous recovery. It was a trigger I couldn't contain. As soon as Martha was "out of the woods" and it was safe for me to surrender my vigilant stance, I started to feel my chemistry go out of whack. I was still in the throes of perimenopause. I was still grieving my mom. There was no way I was ready to lose my sister and be the only woman left in our family. I could almost feel the myelin sheath on my nerves fraying and my mood tanking, but there was nothing I could do to stop it.

This scene was exacerbated by another unanticipated trigger. My twins, now fourteen, began their freshman year at a demanding New England prep school not far from our home. Though they were day students, the school was 90 percent boarders. The administration strongly urged day students to fully immerse themselves in school activities so as not to set up a "town/gown" dynamic.

Also, imagine this: The school had to keep six hundred teen boarders continuously engaged. The kids had academics, sports, performing arts, clubs, and more that kept them away from home for twelve-to-sixteen-hour days and most of the weekends. Our nightly dinners and check-ins vanished. Our Friday night Shabbat celebrations, gone. Our lazy Saturday mornings, over. And the simple joy of them hanging out and doing homework on the kitchen table while I made something simple for dinner was over too.

They were thriving and I was bereft. I had not prepared myself for the proverbial empty nest, yet here it was. I hadn't known how much I depended on those now not-so-little bundles of joy for my emotional uplift. Like so many moms, I had let many of my activities fall by the wayside over the years in favor of being a baseball fan or dance patron, or simply available as a sounding board for their emerging social, political, and intellectual consciousness. Over the last decade, aside from Joe, there was no one else I preferred to be around. And knowing Maya and Sam's time at home would someday be fleeting, I wanted to be totally present for it.

I felt irrationally resentful of the school for stealing my kids, yet they were flourishing in this new environment of challenge and variety. I knew it was best for them, yet I wanted them back.

I felt my mood take a nosedive, and the terror of that familiar rapid descent.

I called Dan.

"Dan, my mood is spiraling."

"Oh, no. Why?"

The billion-dollar question. If only we knew.

Dan and my other sibs had been through this with me so many times before. My dad, now on the verge of ninety-six, had never been much help. He never really got it. Plus, he was already understandably worried about my sister, his primary caretaker since Mom had passed. I couldn't burden him with my fears.

Martha was dealing with her own crisis. I wasn't going to add to her worries. Brother Bill had moved to Florida and was a little out of the loop, absorbed in his own issues. Dan was the one I leaned on; I needed to lean, even though I knew there was nothing he could do to help me.

"I'll send you to my naturopath," he said. "He's amazing with his ability to diagnose. He discovered my body was making almost no lithium, so he put me on a microdose. Come see him. You can stay with Andy and me for the weekend. The sunlight here off Long Island sound is medicinal. You'll feel better."

Dan is a generous guy who, by constitution and temperament, wants to fix things. He usually can. There always has to be a way. I love that about him.

"OK, I'll do that," I say.

I knew he couldn't help.

What ensued was the familiar, frustrating, and terrifying attempt to "tweak" my meds to find the elusive "cocktail" that would restore my brain chemical balance and my sanity.

Frustrating, because there is no clear path out of the woods, no knowing how long it will take, and no knowing whether you will have the stamina to endure it. Terrifying, because the wrong meds make your brain even wackier—or worse. I remembered the time a doctor put me on Effexor—I've learned that this drug can be helpful for some people—but it made my brain feel as if it was bouncing off my skull.

Thankfully, this time I had an ally and partner in Dr. Perlman. I trusted him. I knew he was tenacious and wouldn't give up until I was well, long after I had given up.

If you or someone you love is suffering with a brainstorm, please seek out a doctor worthy of your partnership. While there are many dedicated and skillful psychiatrists like Dr. Perlman out there, there are also many who are painfully (or willfully) uneducated in the bipolar spectrum. Your doctor must listen to you, learn from you, and work tenaciously with you to find the right combination of drugs, therapy, and brain health practices (more on that in Section II) to help you heal.

Getting psychiatric medication "right" is still an art and a science, and it takes a doctor with a rare combination of expertise and humility to succeed. It took me five psychiatrists to get there. I hope it takes you one.

Dr. Perlman and I embarked on the mysterious tour in search of the right meds. First, he put me on Abilify, a drug frequently used to good effect with bipolar patients. A potential side effect of this class of drug (atypical antipsychotics), is tardive dyskinesia, an irreversible facial tick. Although the chances of this were low, the possibility made me even more anxious than I already was. It was counterproductive.

We tried increasing the Lamictal. According to my blood levels, I could go higher. But that left me feeling loopy. My word recall and ability to complete or write sentences went out the window, as did other cognitive capacities. I couldn't stand that. We rolled the dice and decided to decrease the Lamictal.

"I don't know why," Dr. Perlman told me, "but clinically, I'm seeing that some of my patients who were well treated at a certain level of Lamictal can't tolerate that amount in later years. They lose word recall. We'll try going lower."

I respected him for his transparency and honesty, but hearing from an expert that the science was this insufficient added to my sense of hopelessness.

"Jim Phelps does have a new book out, *A Spectrum Approach to Mood Disorders*," Dr. Perlman said. "You may want to have a look at that."

A dim light bulb lit up in my brain, a flicker of hope. I remembered Dr. Phelps as the person who had won my heart and eternal gratitude for his role in curing me in the first place. It had been his diagnostic questionnaire from *Why Am I Still Depressed* that had helped Dr. Perlman diagnose me as definitively bipolar II nine years prior. Of the fourteen questions on the diagnostic questionnaire, I'd had thirteen of them "right."

Dr. Perlman had given me a copy of *Why Am I Still Depressed* at our initial session. For the first draft of this book I'd contacted Dr. Phelps for an interview. I immediately liked and trusted him. Dr. Phelps's author photo shows a mountain guy in outdoor gear. Like me, he'd been an Outward Bound instructor. His writing was accessible and approachable, as was he. I had been exposed to too many self-described "experts" whose real distinction was the size of their ego. My radar was up for incompetence born of arrogance. But Dr. Phelps was the opposite, despite his measurable accomplishments. I admired him for that.

I asked Joe to order his new book that night. The process of ordering anything was beyond me; it was too complicated to figure out where the credit card was or how to get online. The book arrived two days later.

I learned from the introduction that Dr. Phelps had written the book to help therapists and people with bipolar brains navigate the complexity of this syndrome. He described bipolar as a spectrum, not unlike what we now know about sexuality. It's not black or white, gay or straight. There's a whole rainbow of colors in between. Same with the brain, no surprise when you think of it. The cover of Dr. Phelps's new book shows a rainbow.

It was a thick book, intimidating to tackle, but I clung to it, looking for a lifeline, a handhold, a clue as to what I might possibly do to get better. Sometimes, reading it late at night, I noticed that I'd stopped breathing. Some chapters, for example, seemed to indicate I'd never regain sanity.

I called Martha.

"Don't read that stuff before bed," she said compassionately. "You'll get nightmares. He's talking about the majority of research. You're one unique case."

I took to reading it during the day. And there it was—a chapter on the benefits of combining Lamictal with microdoses of lithium in bipolar patients.

I remembered Dan's telling me about taking low doses of lithium after his naturopath determined through blood tests that Dan didn't have enough lithium in his bloodstream.

I knew my mom had been on lithium for decades and it had been a lifesaver. I knew lithium had been the go-to drug for bipolar for decades. I knew I'd been afraid to use it because of its potential scary side effects long-term in large doses. But Dr. Phelps explained that in microdoses, this risk disappeared.

Lithium is a naturally occurring element in nature. I'd been to lithium hot springs in New Mexico. I'd read that towns with lithium in their water had fewer incidents of suicide and higher reports of happiness.

It was worth a try. I showed Dr. Perlman the chapter at my next visit. Though he'd read almost everything on the subject, Dr. Phelps's book was new, and Dr. Perlman had only skimmed it at that point.

"Let's do it," he said. "I have a lot of respect for Phelps's research."

I started with a microdose of lithium along with the Lamictal.

Joe, master of metaphor and son of a stone mason, said, "Maybe it's like bricks and mortar. Separately, they're not worth much. Together you get a solid, impenetrable structure."

Mercifully, I started to feel better.

It's always a combination of things that brings me back into balance. I believe medication is essential to this equation. I will be taking these meds until my dying day and will be grateful every time for their efficacy.

In addition, there are behavioral changes that are key. As the kids approached their sophomore year, I anticipated the empty nest. My cousin Beth, a psychiatric nurse, said, "You have to get busy. Take on more than you think you can. It's better to cancel things than to have empty space on your calendar. You shouldn't wake up any morning without having a place you need to be. Make a plan."

I took her advice. Committed to swimming Mondays, Wednesdays, and Fridays at 7:30 a.m. A walk with friends on Tuesday and Thursdays. I started a book club with another mom at the kids' school, joined a writer's group and a chorus, cocreated a Monday morning chant and prayer group. Get social, get active, get engaged. I maybe overdid it, but I think Beth's advice was brilliant.

Also, by grace of aging, I finally got through perimenopause and arrived in the relatively placid country beyond menopause. My raging hormones calmed down. I was through the whitewater and on to paddling the quiet lake. My brain chemistry could finally balance itself without being pummeled by hormones.

One other thing contributed, in an unseen but immeasurable way, to my healing. In the prologue of this book, I quote the author Terri Cheney, saying, "The disease feeds on shame, shame feeds on silence, and I will not be silent anymore." Though by now I was comfortable telling pretty much everyone about my illness, there were two essential people I had kept this secret from—my children.

In one of my moments of desperation during that year of getting better, I had gone to a spiritual retreat with my Kabbalah teacher, Rabbi Nadya Gross. My fellow students were deeply kind people, and I felt as comfortable as possible, given my current state of anguish.

The retreat took place in the Rockies. The one steady salve I had was walking outside, but never alone, always with someone to ease the pain. My steady walking partner that week was a feisty, wise, former OB-GYN from the Midwest. Jean knew from suffering; she'd been diagnosed with MS twenty years earlier and had lost her career, her first marriage, and much more. She had that brand of wisdom and patience born of survival, and I trusted her. She was one of those people who doesn't hesitate to tell you what to do, even though they've just met you. Yet coming through her unique character, I found this comforting. Bring on the advice, I'm open to anything at this point.

"Have you told your daughter yet?" Jean asked. She was focused on the mother-daughter relationship, even though she knew Sam was in the picture. Maybe she figured Maya would identify with the mother.

"No."

"What?" Jean stopped dead. Turned around and looked at me, incredulous.

"How old is she?"

"Fourteen."

"She's old enough to know. If she finds out from someone else and not you, she'll never forgive you. Why haven't you told her?"

"I'm afraid she'll worry about herself, her future . . ."

"Bullshit," Jean interrupted. "You tell her now or I'm gonna kick your ass."

It took me fifteen months to heed Jean's advice.

But there we were, finally, on a paddling trip in 2017, side by side on kayaks, and calm water, in front of Joe's Minnesota cabin. Maya was now fifteen, her grandmother having passed two years before. She had watched me suffer through that process in wild swings of mood. I'd blamed my grief on Gramma's death and dying process and on menopause, but I had not told her or her brother the full truth. They deserved to know.

"Maya," I began, "do you remember when Gramma was dying, and I was in such a bad place?"

"Of course, Mom."

"And you know how I've told you about dropping out of three grad schools. You thought that was cool, and I said, 'Nope, it wasn't.'"

"Yes."

"Well, all that stuff is related."

"Yeah, I get that."

"Honey, I want you to know something, I have a bipolar brain."

"Oh, OK, Mom . . ."

What followed was an hour and a half of Maya asking me questions in her constitutionally deep, compassionate style. When did it first happen? What did it feel like? Had I suffered much? She was so sorry I'd been through that. And more. It was a rich and rewarding conversation, and I felt huge relief. The proverbial ton of weight lifted from my shoulders. No more shame feeding on silence. No more secrets left. Except one.

"Mom, you're gonna tell Sam, right? You have to tell Sam."

"Yes, I'll tell him next."

When we got back to shore, I found Sam playing Frisbee, his passion, with another pair of twin teen guy buddies.

"Hey, Sammy, can I talk to you for a minute?"

"Sure, Mom, can I finish this game?"

"Yeah, no problem, but then I wanna talk."

"Am I in trouble?"

"No, no, Honey, it's not about that."

Game over and Sam and I walked down the path a little bit to a rock overlooking the water. We were away from phones, electronics, and other distractions. A good place for this conversation.

I began with the same opening I'd had with Maya.

"I have a bipolar brain, Honey."

"Oh, OK, Mom. I'm sorry it's been hard," Sam said, wrapping his arms around me. Sam had surpassed me in height that summer. I noticed for the first time that this embrace was coming from the solid arms of a young man. My son, a compassionate guy. I waited for the next question.

"Do you know what's for lunch?"

You gotta love the contrast.

Between telling the kids, the new medicine, the calming hormones, my sister's recovery, adjusting to my virtually empty nest, and adding all those new practices to fill the void, as well as moving through the grief of my mother's death, I finally found even ground. And got increasingly more stable.

I have been stable ever since.

What's changed this time is that my life aspiration now is balance. Where I used to drive myself to achieve, achieve, achieve . . . where I used to measure my worth based on how many hours I'd worked that day glued to my desk . . . where I used to compete with others for salary or recognition, I just don't anymore. I really don't care anymore. I have to put my health in every dimension first. I value my mental health, my brain vitality over everything else. My family, my marriage, my kids, my communities, my work all depend on it. Everything I might be able to contribute professionally, as a friend, as a neighbor, as mother or wife or sister or daughter or anything else, for that matter, depends on it. Taking care of myself is the smartest, most generous thing I can do. If I get sick, I suck the energy out of the whole system. When I'm well I have a surplus to give.

I want to tell you one of my tricks, my accounting for balance that you might find useful. As I've said, I start almost every day with stretch-and-pray. As my teacher Rabbi Nadya Gross recommends, I end that session with a bit of journaling on the day ahead and the question: How can I be of best service? Then I go through this balance check: I look for where I will get each of the following in my day—ERN (exercise, renewal, and nutrition) and PECS (physical, emotional, creative, and spiritual). I describe these in detail in Part II.

I hope this doesn't seem overwhelming. Over time it's not. For example, with ERN, I check my calendar that day for exercise (e.g., swimming), renewal (essential brain medicine: twenty-minute nap or meditation late afternoon), and nutrition (when/what will I be eating to nourish my brain). If I'll be out all afternoon, I look for a place for a twenty-minute nap break. If I've got back-to-back meetings, I make sure to bring a power bar or something. Always plenty of water as well. I'm prioritizing balance over powering through. I believe it makes all the difference to brain health.

CHAPTER XXI

I'M BIPOLAR II AND A BETTER PERSON BECAUSE OF IT

Although my best friends and my family know about my bipolar brain, being bipolar II rarely comes up in cocktail conversation. I fret over this. Is there ever a right time to come out of the closet as bipolar? Will it affect my reputation, my ability to attract new clients, my work in the world? Yet I'm a better mom, partner, friend, coach, consultant, and business leader because of it. If that's true, why would I be afraid to come forward with my full identity?

There is an enduring stigma around mental illness. Those of us who suffer from brainstorms often don't want other people to know. We fear being vulnerable. We fear other people's judgment.

But here is the truth: The disease that almost robbed me of my life has blessed me. My bipolar II brain has made me a better person. I'm not saying that to be a Pollyanna. No, no, no. It's taken me over two hundred pages of this book to describe the sheer brutality of living with a broken brain, the demon that stalks hour by hour, the sadistic torturer who used to govern my nights and make my days feel like a bottomless hell.

In some ways, having bipolar II is like going to war. Some soldiers don't come back. Others return with posttraumatic stress they'll never recover from. Some imagine suicide, and many go through with it. But then there are some who emerge from the horror and brutality of their experience with a new layer of depth and compassion and sense of service.

These are the survivors, the ones who are able to remember what it was like under enemy fire and counsel those who suffer as they once did. Because in their bones, in their cells, they know what that feels like. They've been there. They can serve.

This is what it feels like for me. I'm a veteran of my own internal wars, a survivor of inner trauma. I bear the wounds of battle. I'm grateful to be alive to tell the tale.

Bipolar II has taught me emotional fearlessness, gratitude, discipline, and compassion. Instead of shame, there is pride. If you have a bipolar brain, I invite you to be proud too.

Emotional Fearlessness

Because you are fluid with the darkness, you can be fully present with other people's fears.

There is no place their fears can take you that you have not been. No matter how scary that place might be for them, it's not for you. You are an able partner and guide. You can accompany them on their journey.

Here's an example: A magnificent woman I know professionally, let's call her Jane, came to me for coaching. Jane was a super accomplished educator, mom, gun control activist, and community leader. I was in awe of her energy. But something was gnawing at her she knew she needed to unpack. She felt intuitively that her passionate work for gun control was driven by fear of social collapse. As we started working together, I learned she is the daughter of two French Holocaust survivors. She had the child-of-survivors syndrome, embodying on a cellular level her parents' trauma. She was terrified for her own two beautiful sons. If disaster struck and society collapsed, the worst imaginable violence, like the violence which had permanently scarred her parents, would be possible, even likely. Her work was driven by this fear. And she knew it wasn't healthy.

I accompanied her in this place as a facilitator and guide. Her terror didn't scare me. I felt honored to be there. The terrorist in my own mind gave me the survivor's perspective, allowing me to understand and be present for Jane as she raged, sobbed, wrestled, and came through the other side with new perspective, clarity, and strength.

Jane's fear of collapse did not go away, but our work together helped her see it for what it was. She has a new relationship to fear. My fearlessness helped her be better able to do her work from a place of passion and commitment, without being incapacitated by fear. I know I could not have been a worthy and capable coach for Jane had I not been a survivor of bipolar II.

Gratitude

Here's what it's like for those of us on the bipolar spectrum: Imagine you wake up every day with an excruciating, immobilizing, headache. Your limbs are too heavy to lift you from your bed. The winds are whipping freezing, icy rain. You're cold, hungry, and thirsty, but you have no food or water. You're chilled to your core.

Now imagine all that lifts. Your headache gone, your limbs loose and agile. The sun is out and there's a balmy, gentle breeze. You have ample fresh water to drink and organic greens from your garden to nourish you.

What happens when you've emerged from that wind-whipping storm into the bird-chirping spring? Gratitude in abundance. Gratitude like a flowing stream. Gratitude that warms your heart and overflows to all those around you.

When colleagues were surprised at my good cheer in the 2020 COVID times (mindful that my attitude is colored by my extreme privilege to live free and safe with food and water and family that I love) and asked me why I was so happy, I explained how the threat of COVID is a walk in the park compared to what my brain has done to me. My brain free and clear? It's a glorious day.

Perhaps like the virus, this gratitude is highly contagious. And that's a good thing. Gratitude is a mood lifter, a force that reorients us to the mystery, wonder, and awe of creation. No wonder so many spiritual practices begin the day with thanks.

The one I know and practice is renewal Judaism, where the entire morning prayer sequence is basically *thank you, thank you, thank you, wow!* Did I remember to say thank you? The prayers are an ancient philosophy that tell us this is how we need to begin our days. And when my brain is good, that's easy. An abundance of gratitude born of bipolar II. Did I ever think I'd say "thank you" for that?

Discipline

If I was an alcoholic at an AA meeting, I'd introduce myself saying, "I'm Sara and I'm an alcoholic." Even if I were forty-years sober, I'd still speak in the present tense. Well, that's how it is for me now. "I'm Sara and I have a bipolar II brain." This I know, though it took me many decades to accept, and will be true until the day I leave this planet. I live with a healthy respect for my bipolar brain. It takes a lot of work and discipline to keep myself mentally healthy.

People who don't know my whole story will often remark, "You're so disciplined. How do you do it?"

"If you knew what was on the other side of this, you'd be too." There are diet disciplines and exercise disciplines and sleep hygiene disciplines that require quality darkness. I receive bodywork, practice mindfulness, and stay on top of supplements and medications. I keep to these disciplines with the vigilance of someone who has a healthy respect for what happens when my brain is out of chemical balance. Over the years I've learned to maintain them without rigidity, but I'm vigilant nonetheless.

Lead by example. Whatever your challenge—physical, emotional, spiritual, I may have a simple and effective practice to help you transform it.

Compassion

There but for the grace of God go I. Absolutely. I will never judge you sitting on the cold concrete in front of our local market with your homeless sign and cup out. I'm pretty sure you've got some variation of the brain I have. It's not your fault. Our US government is merciless in dealing with you. If it hadn't been for my supportive family and good medicine, I could be where you are.

This goes for pretty much any addiction that leads to self-harm. I'm not going to judge you. You are safe with me.

Because I have a bipolar brain, I offer a fearless, disciplined, grateful, and compassionate companion on a journey to the core of what it means to be human. If you've been wrestling with a bipolar brain, this is true for you too.

My hope is that you and your loved ones find this book helpful. I hope that in hearing my story, and seeing yourself in it, you feel less alone. There is hope; there is help. I pray that now, or someday soon, you find your way to balance and joy. That you come to know your own fearlessness, gratitude, discipline, and compassion.

Living on the other side of the storm.

Proud of your unique and beautiful brain.

PART TWO

Now What?

WHAT TO DO IF YOU THINK YOU OR YOUR LOVED ONE HAS A BIPOLAR SPECTRUM BRAIN

PRACTICES FOR
A HEALTHY BRAIN

A s I did for so many years before my accurate diagnosis and
treatment, you may feel hopeless, discouraged, cynical. This
makes total sense! You've tried so many things that have failed.
As much as is humanly possible, have patience and faith. If this
is the first time you are acting on a diagnosis that you are on the
bipolar spectrum, take heart—you will get better.

Think of your therapy and preventative practices as a diamond
with four essential dimensions:

1. Medication prescribed by a doctor with bipolar spectrum
   knowledge
2. Therapy as needed
3. Support network of loving friends and/or family

4. Practices for a healthy brain, what I call *PECS: Physical, Emotional, Creative, and Spiritual.

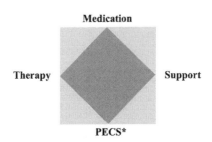

Medication: You have a genetic, biochemical variation in your brain. Surrender to this truth: you cannot cure this on your own. In addition to all other self-care you may be doing, you must find the right medicine to balance your brain chemistry.

Find that psychiatrist who is an expert in bipolar, can prescribe the right medications for you, and who agrees to work closely and in partnership with your therapist. He or she should also have office hours when they can be reached at night and/or return your calls within an hour. You will need their encouragement and support to get through this. (See the DBSA link in Section II below for help in finding a psychiatrist near you.)

Therapy: Find a therapist who understands the bipolar spectrum and therefore the importance of medication (unlike some who are biased against it). She or he ideally works closely or agrees to work closely with a psychiatrist in your area who is an expert in the dynamics of the bipolar spectrum. When in crisis, you may want to see your therapist one or more times a week. It is ideal if he or she is on call via text. Once you are feeling well and in prevention mode, you may need to see this person only on an as-needed basis. My wonderful therapist is on call for me in times of emergency.

Support: Get support from your partner, family, friends. Choose at least one strong advocate who will help you make and keep appointments with health practitioners. Roles for your advocate include making appointments with therapists, taking you to doctors, and organizing your friends and family to cover your basic needs—childcare, food preparation, household income—until you get better. Imagine, heaven forbid, that you had cancer. People would rally to support you in all ways practical and emotional. Though less visible, a bipolar breakdown is that urgent. Ask for and be willing to accept help.

PECS practices for a healthy brain: I use the term PECS as an acronym to remember key practices in four dimensions—another diamond! **Physical, Emotional, Creative, and Spiritual.**

OK, let's get down to it. I am badass disciplined about my self-care. I believe it is absolutely essential to preventing my next bipolar flare. The prospect of that is so terrifying that I am uber dedicated to practices for a healthy brain. When people ask me, "How are you so disciplined?" I usually respond, "I have a healthy respect for my bipolar brain!" A friend who just visited from Minnesota said, "You are my number one model for self-care. You need to tell readers about that in your book."

So here are some of my PECS practices that I offer as a guideline for you. Please don't feel overwhelmed if you can't do all of these. Make them your own. Start with one and work up.

Physical: As you can see by now, I'm fond of acronyms as a memory tool. In the Physical domain it's ERN: Exercise, Renewal, and Nutrition.

Exercise: Moving the body (as you've undoubtedly heard a thousand times) is essential to brain health. Because I'm not an expert in that domain, I won't give you all the scientific data here, but you know the research is out there correlating aerobics and endorphins. You simply feel and look better after a workout.

For me, moving my body is an everyday thing, seven out of seven. Like I said, work your way up if that feels overwhelming. My go-to sports are walking and swimming because they're easy. I live in the woods, so on a good day in the winter I'll go cross-country skiing. You don't have to be an avid athlete. Just move.

If you're feeling down it is hard to get motivated on your own. I'm always better with a buddy. Make dates in advance. It is especially helpful in the winter (if you live in icy territory) to have an appointment with a friend to get you out the door.

I also do yoga daily and have for decades. I missed several months while pregnant and nursing twins, but otherwise I've been consistent with this. I find it extremely nourishing to my otherwise buzz-tending brain to calm down and center. Some would describe this as engaging the parasympathetic nervous system. (Again, I'm not an expert, but there's tons of research connecting yoga and other mindfulness practices to supporting the parasympathetic.) If you don't have a yoga practice yet, there are hundreds of free classes on YouTube. Or find an instructor near you that folks recommend. Start with ten minutes.

Renewal: The afternoon power nap has become an essential part of my practice. I get in a hammock (you can put one up in your apartment), read for ten minutes, then set my alarm for twenty, close my eyes, and I'm out. Turns out there is research to support the idea that naps of under thirty minutes are super healthy for the brain. They act like a mini vacuum cleaner that sucks out metabolic wastes. I go deep and wake up feeling like I've been on vacation. Just half an hour later!

According to an article in the *New York Times* several years back, there's an island in Greece that is home to the highest concentration of folks over one hundred years old in the world. Among other secrets to their success is their required daily nap. (Of course, it helps that the whole island goes to sleep at the same time!)

Growing up, my siblings and I were trained by our dad with his mantra: "Work, work, work, think later!" This also implied "rest later." It took me years to give myself permission to take a break. Now, having trained myself to nap, I can sense and feel when I'm pushing my brain too hard. It takes a while to build that muscle. But once I gave myself permission to respect my brain and take a break when needed, my commitment to doing that strengthened.

Quality rest includes steady sleep. As I've written in previous chapters, I learned the hard way that sleep deprivation is a recipe for disaster for a bipolar brain. In the interview below and on his website, psycheducation.org, Dr. James Phelps also describes the importance of quality darkness during sleep. This means making sure there is no light, including the pervasive little lights on all our electronic phones, alarm clocks, etc. My black silk eye mask is an essential part of my sleep hygiene, and I never leave home without one.

Speaking of little blue lights, it's also imperative to limit screen time at night before bed. The blue light screens emit is bad for the bipolar brain (probably any brain) as we wind down to sleep.

I've heard and read different recommendations, but most say stop screen time two to three hours before bed. If that's too hard, given the ubiquitous nature of screens in our lives, do what you can. You can also pick up inexpensive amber glasses that filter out the dangerous blue light. Note: if you wake up in the middle of the night, do *not* turn on your phone. Keep a book by your bed. Better yet, since it doesn't involve any light, cue relaxing music on headphones before you fall asleep. This works beautifully for me. There's a lot more on sleep hygiene on Dr. Phelps's website. The link is in Part II, Section III.

Nutrition: Again, you've probably heard all this before, but a healthy diet is key. I may be a bit more religious about this than necessary. I go mostly organic. This is influenced by my career in sustainability, where I learned too much about the toxic nature of chemical additives, and because I live in a place surrounded by organic farms. This makes it easy to support my health and my neighbors at the same time. You needn't be exclusively organic but try to avoid processed foods. Here are the things I minimize: white sugar (I use maple syrup), dairy (I go with goat cheese when needed), wheat (except for Friday nights), alcohol (one or two nights a week I have a glass of wine or a beer). I say "minimize," not eliminate, because for my brain and personality, being too rigid about any one path is not useful. That said, I do find that eating a local, mostly organic, low wheat, sugar, and dairy diet is calming for my nervous system.

Next are exercises in the emotional domain to support your brain health.

Emotional: An emotional support system is essential. As I've written elsewhere, find friends who will listen to you without blame or judgment and who will show up for you in a crisis. (You'll do that for them another time.) A therapist is also an essential part of your emotional support system. It's helpful to have a "brain buddy." This is someone you trust fully and who loves you no matter what. Contract with your brain buddy that when you are in crisis you will text them "Code Red." This means that they'll call you immediately.

Before you are in a crisis, create an affirmation for yourself with your brain buddy that you will repeat on a regular basis. The affirmation is stated in the first person, present tense, and with feeling. For example, "I am safe, free, and loved." Or "I am loving, strong, and innocent." You get the point. The important thing is that the affirmation rings true for you and gives you a sense of calm and joy.

Here's a five-step process for working with your brain buddy in a time when you are under stress:

Step 1: Notice what's happening in your body/emotions and give it a name you state out loud. For example, "Self-judgment is arising." "Comparing-mind is arising." "Fear is arising."

The key point here is that by stating the uncomfortable feeling as "arising" we separate it from ourselves and see it for what it is, a temporary state of mind. It does not own or define us. This three-word formula, "_____ [Negative emotion or sensation] is arising" works because it is simple and accessible in a moment of crisis. (Shout out to MBCT, Mindfulness Based Cognitive Therapy out of UMass Worcester for this approach.)

Step 2: When you state: "Fear (or other) is arising," that's your trigger to text your brain buddy, "Code Red."

Step 3: Your brain buddy calls and states your affirmation with you out loud, slowly, several times. This calms your nervous system and lets you know in the moment that you're not alone.

Step 4: Make a plan with your brain buddy for immediate next steps to get through the crisis.

Step 5: Exhale and celebrate yourself for implementing this triage plan.

Creative: It is helpful for our brains to have creative outlets to minimize perseveration and to maximize a sense of productive engagement, purpose, and meaning. Everyone has their own creative go-to practices. For me these are writing (working that one now), cooking, and singing.

For others it might be painting, performing, and gardening. It might be political activism or volunteer engagement. Work of the heart involving some service to others is particularly therapeutic. It's ideal if some of your activities take place in community because that supports the emotional side of PECS. For example, I often write in a writer's group. This provides both creative engagement and social connection. There's no specific recipe here (unless you are cooking). Just find something that has meaning for you.

Spiritual: I could write a whole other book here. (Indeed, I have. It's called *Secrets of the Seventh Day*, about the power of unplugging for one day every week.) You may or may not have a religious practice or belief in what AA calls a "Higher Power." If you do, that's great. If not, that's OK too. Practicing with a spiritual community is powerful because it supports both the Emotional and Spiritual side of PECS. Find a trustworthy (not a guru) spiritual teacher. You may engage in mindfulness meditation, nature walks, morning prayers, or any other spiritual discipline that expands the mind. Choose what works for you.

One spiritual discipline I do recommend to everyone irrespective of religion or background is a daily gratitude practice. I do that every morning on waking (aided by my teacher Shefa Gold's app) and most nights before falling asleep, when I remember. One year I did an experiment and wrote one thank you letter a day for sixty days. This generated all kinds of positive energy that I did not anticipate. Here's what I learned:

1. Offering gratitude is a big gift to those on the receiving end. They are reminded of their beauty. Who couldn't use that?
2. This blessing is contagious. They see their glory and tend to "pay it forward" to the next person.
3. Giving thanks shifts our consciousness from scarcity, pain, and victimhood, to abundance, joy, and possibility.

Try it. It's liberating.

Yes, if you have a bipolar brain, these PECS practices for a healthy brain are a lifelong commitment. Being disciplined in your commitment to self-care is a required part of your prevention program. Taking the time to do this is not selfish. It is essential to your well-being. The good news is that no matter who you are, you will be healthier and happier for it.

If you are just beginning on the PECS** path, start small and celebrate every step. You are putting you and your unique and powerful brain first. Good job!

** If you or someone you love would like support in implementing the PECS practices, please reach out to me at SaraSchley.com.

RESOURCES—WEB, BOOKS, YOUTUBE

Two Powerful Websites:

I. My first go to, and the place I send folks who ask, is Dr. James Phelps and Dr. Chris Aiken's psycheducation.org. This offers a wealth of resources, and I highly encourage you to explore it in detail. Four links I find particularly important are:

   1. **Bipolar Diagnostic Scale (BPDS)**—Recognizing and Managing the Dynamics of bipolar II
        If you are wrestling with your brain, this is a powerful self-diagnostic which gives you data to present to your family and health-care provider. Take this simple quiz to validate your hunch that you may be living on the bipolar spectrum.

2. Quality darkness:

   I've been surprised to learn from doctors like Dr. Phelps that the quality of darkness during sleep is a major factor in mitigating and preventing bipolar flares. Find fascinating research at this link. The bottom line: I sleep every night with a silk mask over my eyes. Find more here on limiting "blue light" from computers and more.

3. Diagnosis in the Mood Spectrum

   This article is an accessible exploration of the bipolar spectrum.

4. Basics of Bipolar Treatment

   Gives an overview of three most important principles in treatment.

There is much more on this site to explore.

II. Depression Bipolar Support Alliance

DBSA (www.dbsalliance.org), is a highly regarded, national peer-to-peer network. Put your zip code in their search engine to find a support person near you. From their website: "DBSA offers peer-based, wellness-oriented support and empowering services and resources available when people need them, where they need them, and how they need to receive them—online 24/7, in local support groups, in audio and video casts, or in printed materials distributed by DBSA, our chapters, and mental health-care facilities across America."

Again, put your zip code in their search engine to find a live support person near you.

Books:

- *Bipolar II Disorder Recognition, Understanding, and Treatment* by Dr. Holly Swartz and Dr. Trisha Suppes
- *Why Am I Still Depressed?* by Dr. James Phelps
- *A Spectrum Approach to Mood Disorders,* by Dr. James Phelps
- *An Unquiet Mind,* by Dr. Kay Redfield Jamison

YouTube: *An awesome YouTube channel*

- *What Kind of Depression Do You have?* YouTube Series by Dr. James Phelps and colleagues. Super helpful and accessible descriptions of the bipolar spectrum.

INTERVIEW WITH
DR. JAMES PHELPS,
BIPOLAR SPECTRUM EXPERT

The following interview with Dr. James Phelps, author of numerous seminal works on the bipolar spectrum including *Bipolar Not So Much* and *Why Am I Still Depressed?* was recorded on June 5, 2019. Dr Phelps's bipolar Diagnostic Scale, and the diagnosis that followed from the results of that profound test saved my life.

Sara Schley (SS): How did you get interested in this particular work? Did you have any personal experience with bipolar or depression?

Dr. James Phelps (JP): Remarkably, in my residency training I had almost no formal training in bipolar disorders at all. It was a big gap. When I started practicing in the hospital system, where I've been working for the last nearly thirty years, I was doing inpatient work halftime, outpatient work halftime. I discovered pretty quickly that people were being admitted over and over again—a revolving door—with a diagnosis of bipolar disorder, and it was not a territory I knew well. So I started to educate myself more.

The further I got into treating people, I discovered there was no clear outer margin to bipolar disorder, in that a person doesn't have to meet the DSM criteria for mania to potentially respond well to bipolar medication. Then I came across substantial literature defining bipolar spectrum disorder.

SS: So, you didn't have any experience, like in your own family, of bipolar? I first started researching this before I was ever hit with it personally because my mom was depressed, and I wanted to learn more.

JP: No, it was through professional exposure. Well, I had some folks, people I knew who, in retrospect might have had some kind of bipolar disorder, one close friend in high school—his diagnosis was temporal lobe epilepsy, but in retrospect I think it might have been a bipolar variant. I got into psychiatry in a very circuitous way, and then I just kept seeing people admitted to the hospital over and over and they seemed to get better outcomes when they were taken off antidepressants and put on mood stabilizers.

SS: To what degree do you think your colleagues—psychiatrists and therapists—are knowledgeable about the bipolar spectrum now? The bipolar II distinction?

JP: There is a spectrum. Some completely "get" it, recognize that bipolarity is a dimensional phenomenon, that there is a spectrum. Some completely reject the idea and say that it will lead to the breakdown of our diagnostic system, that if we take the idea of bipolar too far it will weaken our ability to help people who are bipolar I in particular and will blend into borderline personality disorder. They get quite rigid about hanging on to the "rule." You can see this spectrum in the literature. The irony is that these ways of looking at the phenomena are not mutually exclusive! One can use DSM criteria, and also use the spectrum—not *are* they bipolar but *how* bipolar are they?

SS: Are some professionals simply not aware, just don't know about the spectrum? About fifteen years ago, one of my psycho-therapists, a lovely person, later apologized profusely and said she was sorry, but she just didn't know about bipolar II at the time of our work together. Then she told me I had to write this book.

JP: Bipolar II is certainly in the psychiatric literature at this point, in the DSM. There are not many psychiatrists who don't understand the concept. It is unfortunate, among therapists, a lot of folks who trained more than fifteen years ago really don't understand the phenomenon at all even though they see a lot of it. Probably about 50 percent of them, maybe even 80 percent, are not aware. Because bipolar II is like depression, but with something else. If you don't recognize it, you will just think that it's a version of depression. They don't know that there's something else they should be looking for. It is the same problem among primary care doctors. Probably 90 percent of them don't know they should screen for bipolarity *before* they give someone an antidepressant.

In 1994 the DSM4 included bipolar II. If you came into your medical or therapy practice before 1994 there was no opportunity for you to learn about it. Who is prescribing the antidepressants? The primary care doctors. Twenty-five years later we are still in the process of helping primary care doctors learn about it! Somewhere around 2001 I started thinking that giving antidepressants and patients getting worse from them is a big problem. I created a website psycheducation.org in about 2001, explaining this to doctors.

(Sara's note: This is a massively important and useful resource for everyone concerned with the bipolar spectrum.)

One out of ten adults in the US are taking an antidepressant, 11% of the population. It's an epidemic. If 5 or 10% of those people actually have bipolar II disorder, we're talking about making a lot of people worse! The magnitude of this problem is so much bigger than people understand.

SS: About three million if I'm doing the math right.

JP: Right.

SS: So it seems like this book is not only important for people who are suffering but also for the doctors they go to, the counselors, the primary care doctors. Psychiatrists have a stigma, so people go first to their primary care doctor or the therapist. We have a big target audience for this book.

JP: Yes, you do! The story is not that different now from when you were struck with the disorder in the 1980s. How are we doing? We are doing horribly! Doctors have to screen for bipolar disorder when people present with depression. And for the most part, they are not.

It's not working to reach out directly to the primary care docs, they don't have time to read all of this. You have to reach the patients and their families.

SS: Your website talks about preventative and alternative therapeutic methodologies in addition to medication. What do you recommend? What are the top five things you want people to know that they should be doing?

JP: Number One: How are you sleeping? If it's badly, address that. How? Regularize your sleep schedule. Regular bedtime, regular rise time, gradually push that to what is more natural—nearer to sunset and sunrise. Natural bipolar disorder folks tend toward being night owls. Going to bed earlier, getting up earlier, is extremely difficult for many people. How do you do it? You can manipulate your exposure to light and darkness—that helps some. You also need a major behavioral effort to coach yourself into an earlier rise time. A dawn simulator helps, but most people have never heard of it. It is successful, simple, and cheap.

SS: In my experience, when my bipolar flares are at their worst, the only peace I got was late at night, so I'd stay up late. I learned from your book that steady sleep is so important. Now I tell people

I must have my afternoon power nap; my brain needs it. And I wear one of those silk masks over my eyes all the time.

JP: It is similar to medication. Once you get things well controlled, we think maybe you can back off on it a bit and see how it goes. You figure out a sleep pattern, you hammer in a sleep regimen, and now that you're well you can back off on the rigidity a bit and see how it goes. Maybe you start to unravel and adjust back up a little more.

SS: Strategy Number Two? We got our sleep down, what do we do next?

JP: I'm having difficulty with a short answer because there is a paper coming out from the International Society on Bipolar Disorders (ISBD) on chronotherapy. It's the broader subject of how to manipulate your circadian rhythm without medication. Light and darkness are part of it, a regular pattern of sleep is part of it, and there are additional tools, like a light box. But this is what we would add on later—a regular pattern of sleep with deliberate exposure to lightness and darkness to facilitate that.

SS: My daughter was born with a blood vessel wrapped around her trachea. She is doing amazingly well twenty years later and after life-saving surgery at age seven. But when she was a baby, I had to stay up all night with breathing treatments to save her life. Later I learned from you that sleep deprivation was a recipe for disaster for my bipolar brain.

JP: What would we tell someone like you now? If you have to be up in the middle of the night like that? Get rid of the blue lighting. A simple treatment, but one that's not part of our treatment lexicon at all. You can wear amber lenses or get some amber night lights and light bulbs. It's really simple. Just buy a bulb that doesn't put out any blue light at all! It is so much closer to natural light. People will know this in fifteen years.

A little-known fact, 50 percent of women with bipolar disorder get postpartum depression. In part it is preventable because often they are staying up late at night taking care of their infants in an environment with blue lighting. They need a no-blue environment.

SS: Wow. I wish I'd known that! This is a kind of crazy question, but I keep wondering . . . why? If life selects for advantages, what is the purpose of depression? Why is it there?

JP: You can imagine a reason for hypomania, well that can be adaptive because everyone else in the cave is asleep, kind of hibernating through the winter, and you're awake and planning for the future, excited about, "We can get that bison if we just . . ." or wondering about climbing under the rug with that woman over there—so there are advantages perhaps of being hypomanic, but what is the advantage of being depressed? Some people say it's adaptive because when you're facing social stresses maybe it's good to just kind of conserve your resources, hunker down, and wait for a better time.

Here's the explanation that makes more sense to me: At the time we were evolving as a species, infection was a big threat to survival. You have to fight it with everything your immune system has got. Throw yourself down and don't be motivated to do anything. Then the body dedicates all its resources to fighting infection. That's adaptive.

SS: Can you tell us about epigenetics? Are there environmental influences, nature nurture, that encourage genes to turn on and off, and the corollary is what can parents do to maximize health for their children—this gene not firing? I grew up in a trauma household. My kids are not growing up in a trauma household and I'm hoping that will be preventative!

JP: If there is anything to the notion that one's genes are changed through environmental experience, then what gene changes make people more vulnerable to mood disorder? The gene changes associated with trauma. So, what are you going to do, if the story is true that you can be changing your children's genes? Keep them from being exposed to horrible trauma. Be the best parent you can be.

SS: Do you think there's any relationship between historical trauma of an ethnic or other group sometimes referred to as "cellular memory"? For instance, I'm an Ashkenazi Jew, and it seems as if there is more depression or bipolar among us, as well as in African Americans and Native Americans who have gone through unspeakable trauma.

JP: That's a fascinating and important question. It hinges on the epigenetic idea. Surely someone has data on this. I do not. I encourage us to take an unbiased look at the literature to see if it's true.

(Sara's note: Since this interview, *My Grandmother's Hands: Racialized Truama and a Pathway to Mending our Hearts and Bodies* by psychotherapist Resmaa Menakem. Manekam quotes Dr. Rachel Yehuda of Mount Sinai Hospital. Her original research sheds light on the relationship between trauma, epigenetics, bipolar, and other brain challenges. A powerful and healing read.)

SS: What's the next frontier for research, treatment, and destigmatizing in the field?

JP: First, let's continue the work in the study of nonmedication approaches for the treatment of bipolar disorder. Much more work needs to be done in this area. One reason bipolar disorder is so stigmatized, is that the treatment options are so frightening. If you make the treatment not so scary, people won't be so afraid of considering the possibility of bipolarity. You hear the word "lithium," and it sounds scary from the get-go. That's part of the stigma.

SS: What do you think about the actual brain research that is being done now? Is there promise for better research that would help the medications be more laser-like?

JP: I certainly thought I'd see it by now. Treatment of bipolar disorder now is like treatment of diabetes before physicians understood insulin, when they did not know or understand that diabetes was a lack of insulin. We have been fumbling around in the dark. I did think that by the time I would be bringing my professional life to a close, we wouldn't be wandering around in the dark so much, but we are! Why is it that someone can get manic, and then later get depressed? What is the mechanism? There must be a busted switch. Shouldn't we be able to find that switch? It is turning out to be so much more complicated. It is a disappointment to me that I might not be alive to see the answer. The answer is coming in little pieces.

Reaching the moon is still a way off. Meantime, we can start by assessing, "How bipolar are you?" That alone would advance our efforts to help people so much and that is within our reach now.

SS: Because of the stigma around mental illness, it has received fewer research dollars. If we had more funding, could we figure it out—get to the moon—sooner?

JP: Certainly.

SS: Is there anything else you would like readers to know?

JP: There is a very simple thing practitioners can do right now. Look for bipolarity before giving antidepressants. It is staring us in the face. First, do no harm. That is the central message in the story my colleagues and I want to convey. What we are describing is an epidemic with a solution within our control. The epidemic is we're giving all these people with bipolar II antidepressants, and they don't work. Stop doing that.

I wrote a paper with others in 2008 about the idea that bipolarity is a spectrum, not a yes or no, and now we are finally getting somewhere with the adoption of this idea! It's beginning to dawn on doctors that we need to have a different approach when someone shows up who is depressed. We are getting there, Sara. If you can get this book out there far and wide, it will be a big help.

SS: Thank you!

JP: Thank you.

REMOVING THE SHAME—SOME FAMOUS PEOPLE WITH BIPOLAR (THERE ARE MANY MORE!)

Here's a partial list, thanks to Wikipedia, as of 2021. Apparently, we are not as alone as we think we are!

+ Alvin Ailey, American choreographer, diagnosed with bipolar disorder (then called manic depression)
+ Sherman Alexie, Native American poet, writer, and filmmaker
+ Adam Ant, English musician and actor
+ Emilie Autumn, American singer and violinist
+ Maria Bamford, American comedian, stated in an interview with the *Salt Lake Tribune* that she has been diagnosed with bipolar II disorder.

+ Maurice Benard, actor, discussed his diagnosis on *The Oprah Winfrey Show*, and has since become active in promoting bipolar awareness.
+ Paul Boyd, classical animator
+ Ronald Braunstein, American orchestra conductor and cofounder of the ME2/Orchestra for individuals like himself who suffer from mental illness.
+ L. Brent Bozell Jr., American conservative activist and writer. He wrote publicly about his experiences with and recovery from bipolar disorder.
+ Russell Brand, British comedian, actor, radio host, author, and activist.
+ Chris Brown, American singer, songwriter, rapper, dancer, and actor, Brown has been diagnosed with bipolar II disorder.
+ Tiffany Lee Brown, American writer, artist, and musician
+ Art Buchwald, humorist and Pulitzer Prize winner
+ Mariah Carey, American singer-songwriter. Diagnosed with bipolar II disorder in 2001.
+ Akio Chiba, Japanese manga artist, committed suicide due to issues related to bipolar disorder.
+ Mary Ellen Copeland, PhD, author, educator and mental health advocate
+ Francis Ford Coppola, American film director, producer, and screenwriter, was diagnosed by a psychiatrist as having bipolar disorder.
+ John Curtin, 14th Prime Minister of Australia (1941–1945).
+ Robert Downey Jr., American actor and film producer.

- Richard Dreyfuss, actor, appeared in a BBC documentary to talk about his experience with the disorder.
- Patty Duke, actress, author, and mental health advocate.
- Thomas Eagleton, United States Senator from Missouri. He was privately diagnosed with bipolar type II in 1983, eleven years after stepping down as George McGovern's running mate during the latter's presidential campaign in 1972 due to the revelation of Eagleton receiving electro-convulsive therapy in the 1960s.
- Carrie Fisher, actress and writer. Starred in the *Star Wars* films as Princess Leia.
- Zelda Fitzgerald, American socialite and novelist; wife of American author F. Scott Fitzgerald. Diagnosed during her life with schizophrenia; now thought likelier to be bipolar disorder.
- Larry Flynt, publisher and the president of Larry Flynt Publications (LFP).
- Ellen Forney, graphic artist and cartoonist. Creator of the autobiographic comic, *Marbles: Madness, Depression, Michelangelo, and Me.*
- Jennifer Frey, journalist
- Stephen Fry, actor, comedian
- Selena Gomez, American singer, songwriter, and actress. Revealed her bipolar diagnosis in April 2020 in an Instagram livestream with Miley Cyrus.
- Matthew Good, Canadian musician. He first disclosed his illness in a personal blog
- Graham Greene, English novelist

- Suzy Favor Hamilton, American former middle distance runner
- Doug Harvey, Canadian professional ice hockey player
- Ernest Hemingway, American journalist. Won the Pulitzer Prize (1953) and the Nobel Prize in Literature (1954) for his novel *The Old Man and the Sea*. He was diagnosed with bipolar disorder and insomnia in his later years. He committed suicide in 1961.
- Abbie Hoffman, political activist, anarchist
- Jesse Jackson Jr., former member of the United States House of Representatives, has stated he's been diagnosed with bipolar II disorder.
- Kay Redfield Jamison, American clinical psychologist, professor of psychiatry and writer, has written extensively about her personal experiences with bipolar disorder, including in *An Unquiet Mind*.
- Patrick J. Kennedy, former member of the United States House of Representatives, has spoken on his mental health issues, including diagnosed bipolar disorder.
- Margot Kidder, American actress
- John Konrads, Australian freestyle swimmer
- David LaChapelle, American commercial photographer, fine-art photographer, music video director, film director, and artist
- Vivien Leigh, English actress, most famous for her role as Scarlett O'Hara in David O. Selznick's movie *Gone with the Wind*
- Jenifer Lewis, American actress, spoke about her diagnosis on *Oprah* in September 2007.

- Elizabeth Manley, Canadian former competitive figure skater
- Emily Martin, sinologist, anthropologist, feminist, professor at New York University; drew on her own experience with bipolar disorder to write *Bipolar Expeditions: Mania and Depression in American Culture.*
- Kim Novak, actress
- Isaac Newton, English physicist, mathematician, astronomer, theologian, author. Inventor of calculus; formulator of the laws of motion and universal gravitation.
- Phil Ochs, singer-songwriter, political activist. Committed suicide at age 36.
- Nicola Pagett, actor. Wrote about her bipolar disorder in her autobiography *Diamonds Behind My Eyes.*
- Jane Pauley, TV presenter and journalist. The former *Today* and *Dateline* host describes being diagnosed with bipolar disorder in her 2004 autobiography *Skywriting: A Life Out of the Blue*, as well as on her short-lived talk show.
- Sylvia Plath, poet and writer, may have experienced bipolar disorder.
- Edgar Allan Poe, poet and writer, may have experienced bipolar disorder.
- Jackson Pollock, American artist
- Emil Post, American mathematician and logician. He is best known for his work in the field that eventually became known as computability theory. Post was bipolar and had his first attack in 1921. For the rest of his life he had to be periodically hospitalized and given electroshock—the standard treatment at that time.

- Rene Rivkin, entrepreneur
- Charlie Sheen, American actor
- Nina Simone, American singer
- Naomi Sims, American model, businesswoman, and author, widely credited as being the first African-American supermodel
- Frank Sinatra, American singer and actor. "Being an 18-karat manic-depressive, and having lived a life of violent emotional contradictions, I have an overacute capacity for sadness as well as elation."
- Yo Yo Honey Singh, Indian rapper, music producer, singer, and film actor
- Harry Smith, American Olympian
- Britney Spears, American singer, songwriter, and dancer
- Alonzo Spellman, American football player
- Dusty Springfield, English pop singer
- Ben Stiller, American actor
- Margaret Trudeau, Canadian celebrity and ex-wife of former Canadian Prime Minister Pierre Elliot Trudeau. She now travels throughout Canada and other countries speaking out against the stigmas on mental illness.
- Ted Turner, American media businessman. Founder of CNN.
- Jean-Claude Van Damme, Belgian actor and martial artist
- Vincent van Gogh, artist
- Townes Van Zandt, singer-songwriter
- Mark Vonnegut, author
- James Wade, English professional darts player

- Ayelet Waldman, Israeli-American novelist and essayist, has written about her bipolar II disorder.
- Ruby Wax, American actress, mental health campaigner, lecturer, and author
- Norman Wexler, screenwriter
- Brian Wilson, musician and founding member of The Beach Boys
- Amy Winehouse, English singer-songwriter
- Jonathan Winters, American comedian, actor, author, and artist
- Virginia Woolf, writer
- Catherine Zeta-Jones, Welsh actress, has bipolar II disorder.

AFTERWORD

—HOLLY A. SWARTZ, MD
Professor of Psychiatry, University of Pittsburgh School of Medicine

In *BrainStorm*, author Sara Schley pairs her prodigious writing talents with a compelling story of hardship, personal suffering, and redemption. She describes devastating depressions, including one triggered by the "triple threat" of falling into a ravine, infertility problems, and work stress. She reports on the agonizing toll that mood swings take on families, first experienced by herself as a child in the wake of her mother's bipolar disorder and later by her own children as depression gripped Schley soon after their birth. She describes a difficult quest to find appropriate psychiatric care, including run-ins with quackery (exorcism, psychics, and crystals) as well as conventional medical debacles such as medication-induced hypomania. She speaks of spiritual renewal, personal growth, and the blessings of family and friends. Recounting a roller coaster of highs and lows with nail-biting outcomes, it may seem that Schley has written a suspenseful work of fiction. But those who know bipolar II disorder—part of the bipolar spectrum—understand that *BrainStorm* is anything but fiction.

As a psychiatrist who specializes in the treatment of bipolar II disorder, I can confirm that Schley's memoir accurately captures the journey faced by many individuals with this illness. Millions of individuals suffer from bipolar II disorder (approximately 1% of the population), and yet it is underrecognized and understudied. Like Schley, many with bipolar II disorder contend with years of misdiagnoses, inappropriate treatments, and untreated mood. On average, eleven years elapse from the start of bipolar II symptoms to correct diagnosis. During those intervening years, many struggle with an improperly managed illness that often gets worse before it gets better. Because this disorder typically onsets in early adulthood—as was the case for Schley—lost decades often coincide with formative years when individuals are trying to establish themselves vocationally and interpersonally. Without proper treatment, illness-related mood fluctuations can derail foundational careers and relationships.

Like so many others with bipolar II disorder, Schley's evolving understanding of her illness, including finding trusted professionals to support her wellness, took decades. She discovered that many mental health professionals lack knowledge about bipolar II disorder and learned that the illness can masquerade as "regular depression" before even a savvy doctor recognizes it as bipolar II. Even when her diagnosis became clearer, Schley was reluctant to take medications, which continued to put her health at risk. She was troubled by the enormous emotional burden borne by her loved ones, and she was reluctant to disclose her illness because of the unfair stigma still associated with brain disorders. These struggles are unfortunately all too common among those with bipolar II disorder.

If the challenges so poignantly described by Schley in *BrainStorm* sound familiar to those knowledgeable about bipolar II disorder, her unflappable resolve in the face of these challenges comes across as uniquely Schley. Even when dangling precariously from a rock in Mexico, she never let go. She asked for help when needed, found a reliable social support network, and sought answers from professionals even when some had betrayed her trust. She used her difficult experiences with bipolar II disorder as an opportunity for growth, impressively sharing with readers strategies that help her stay well (daily exercise, spiritual renewal, regular sleep, and good nutrition) when deployed in conjunction with medication. I was especially moved by the gratitude she expressed throughout her memoir and her emphasis on compassion for self and others. In short, this memoir is as much an inspiring road map for achieving and maintaining health in the face of illness as it is a catalogue of the perils of bipolar II disorder.

Schley began her book with the story of a friend who recently lost her nephew with bipolar II disorder to death by suicide. After reading Schley's memoir, the friend responds, "If I had read this manuscript, my nephew might be alive." Many individuals with bipolar I disorder, which differs significantly from bipolar II disorder, find solace and understanding in Kay Redfield Jamison's great memoir, *An Unquiet Mind*, but for those with bipolar II disorder, there were no comparable resources. Before *BrainStorm*, there was no well-written book describing lived experiences with bipolar II disorder. Schley's memoir offers hope to others who are experiencing bipolar II disorder, including those whose illness has yet to be properly diagnosed. From her own experiences of depression, difficulty finding a doctor who understood her illness, and family struggles, Schley conveys both the confusion of the illness and a way forward toward better understanding.

Her journey underscores the importance of early detection and appropriate treatment; it also serves as a testament to the power of perseverance and determination. Schley's fortitude, gratitude, and openness are remarkable; she has much to say that is inspiring to all of us. Although her friend's nephew is no longer able to benefit from this extraordinary memoir, no doubt many others with bipolar II disorder will know after reading *BrainStorm* that they are not alone. Because of Schley, they will come to realize that, with proper support and resources, they, too, can not only survive but also thrive with bipolar II disorder.

ACKNOWLEDGMENTS

It has taken a lifetime of family, friends, colleagues, teachers, and more to allow me to survive, and even thrive, with this bipolar brain. Thank you to every single soul in my Women's Circle of twenty-six years, to the "Wild Women," to our "Mom's over 40" group, the "Women Sustainability Leaders," and our "Jewish Group of the Valley." Every one of you has shown up in times of dire need.

Sara Acker, you rallied the community when I was gasping for air, and you were my crisis hotline 24/7. Annette Cycon, you drove me to doctors and put meals in my freezer. Lynn Davis, you were an on-call, steady voice of compassion and faith. Andi Waisman, you checked in every Wednesday morning. Marsia Harris and Amber Gurley, you showed up with full, loving hearts to take care of the kids when I was not capable. Sara Acker, Jenny Coy, Chris Labich, Deborah Mager, you helped me raise those kids with so much love, generosity, and joy. Where would I be without you? Mishy Lesser and Chris Ives, you were the godparents of dreams, jumping in to be present for Sam and Maya on a moment's notice. Mira Nussbaum, thank you for your abundance of love and for getting me through my last breakdown when my parents were dying. Betsy Hinden, Melissa Lukin, Nina Begosian, and Heidi Berke, you were the women I felt safe to lean into when the terror of bipolar first flared in my early twenties. No surprise—most of you became the magnificent psychologists that you are. Thank you.

The writing also occurs in community. Thanks, beyond thanks, to Mara Bright for being midwife to and first editor of *BrainStorm* and my "hike and write" partner for more than two decades. Thanks to editors Jennifer Margulies and Kitty Axelson. And especially Kitty, for recognizing that this story had to be published and giving of her time and expertise to make it happen. Patricia Lee Lewis, you introduced me to the Amherst Writers and Artist approach and celebrated everything about me as a writer. Thanks, Mark Williams, when you said, "Write, Sara, write!" I believed you. To my original writing teacher and mentor, Margaret Metzger of blessed memory who said, "I know what I feel when I see what I write." Thus, initiating a lifetime practice of writing as emotional healing.

Wind in my sails Linda Booth Sweeney and Stephanie Ryan, for three decades you have been my rockstar support and inspiration in our shared global-systems change endeavors. Writers too, you insisted that this book had to get out there to save lives. Rose Penelope Yee, your endless generosity and fierce support is such a blessing. You will always be my mayor. To Rose, Kim Coupounas, and all the women of WeTheChange thank you for showing me what badass women leaders, who are passionate about making a better world, can do together.

Acknowledgments

To readers of early drafts of this manuscript, your thoughtful critique made it much better. And your enthusiasm for its message gave me the courage to continue. To Mara Bright, Joe Laur, Nancy Roosa, Mishy Lesser, Bonnie Waltch, Marilyn Paul, Nancy Knudsen, Leslie Gell, Jeff Weston, Darcy Winslow, and James Harrison: thank you.

On the emotional healing plane, thanks to Cliff Barry for creating and teaching Shadow Work®, and to my fellow circle of practitioners and champions, ALisa Starkweather, Jude Blitz, Janine Romaner, Nicola Kurk, Becky Schupbach, Sarita Chawla and Mira Nussbaum. You have healed lifetimes of wounds. For spiritual richness, depth, guidance, wisdom, and inspiration, thank you to my teachers Rabbis Shefa Gold and Nadya Gross, and to our wonderful band of "spirit buddies" of Kol Zimra and Wisdom School. Ariel Lippman, you have provided support and inspiration every new moon since 2008.

Thank you, Dr. Perlman. When you diagnosed me with bipolar II you saved my life. And thank you to Dr. James Phelps, whose books describing the bipolar spectrum were critical lifesavers. Dr Phelps's early belief in this project and the urgency of getting its message out was huge encouragement over several years. The powerful support of Drs. Holly Swartz and Trisha Suppes—global thought leaders in understanding bipolarity—helped me to believe in the importance of amplifying the message of this first-person narrative, written by someone with a bipolar II brain. Dr. Ange DiBenedetto, therapist extraordinaire, thank you for inspiring me to write this memoir in the first place when you said, "My colleagues need to hear your story." You have been there for me and Joe as bedrock support for fifteen years and counting.

To my mom, Harriet Wald Schley, thank you for giving me your blessing to tell this story before you passed in 2015. The book includes painful and vulnerable moments of your own struggle with mental illness. It was courageous and generous of you to say "Yes" to this project.

Thanks to my siblings, Martha, Bill, and Dan, who accompanied me on the journey of living with and through the experience of being children of a mom with undiagnosed, severe bipolar, as well as a dad with his own trauma-induced challenges. You have always been there when I needed you most. Martha, you saved my life when you found Dr. Perlman.

To Sean, Melanie, and Lauren, thank you for accepting me and loving me when I came into your lives twenty-nine years ago and remained ever since. You've made me a better mom, and I am so proud of the people and parents you have become.

Maya and Sam, you have given my life more joy, "naches," and love than you can imagine. Thank you for your emphatic, enthusiastic, immediate, and unrelenting encouragement. ("You have to publish this, Mom; it will save lives!") Your persistent championing of this book when my own will was flailing gave me energy to complete it. You bless my life every day, and I am so proud of the beautiful people you are. I love you to the universe and back.

Joe, you got a chapter named for you. You were and are my rock. Thank you for all the ways in which you show up with love every single day. I love you beyond the beyond.

ABOUT THE AUTHOR

S ara Schley is an international business consultant,
speaker, and author who has led
organizational transformations
at renowned companies around
the world. She is a mother,
grandmother, community leader,
and has been married to a great
guy for twenty-six years. She also
has a Bipolar II brain, on the
Bipolar Spectrum.

Sara has kept this mostly secret for four decades. Until now. She
is choosing to tell her riveting story—from broken to blessed—to
save lives, end the stigma, and optimize healing for millions.

Sara lives in the hill towns of Western Massachusetts with
her husband, loyal lab, and a steady flow of friends and family.
Reach out to Sara at www.saraschley.com.

Made in the USA
Coppell, TX
12 August 2022

81362732R10157